THE SECOND CASUALTY

or, A Youth in Asia

by Tom MacLean

SPIRIT OF 1950-52

Tom

5505 Colorado Drive

Concord, CA 94521

Dear Reader,

This novel relates as truthfully as possible the details of my life from 1949 to 1952. As a 16-year-old I escaped from a bad family situation via the deus ex machina of the mobilization of the Oklahoma National Guard during the Korean Conflict.

My intention has been to recreate my experiences of training in Louisiana, occupation duty in Japan, and conflict in Korea. I have recorded the day-to-day incidents as a story but with a conscious effort to avoid fictionalization.

As an 18-year-old GI Bill English major I was taught and believed my lecturer's assertion that such a record as mine, of individual experience literally recorded, alone is insufficient to represent any more than a limited inferior truth. I accepted the analogy that an artist takes the formless raw clay of his experience and at his desk produces a pinch pot of higher fictional truth.

But a half dozen years ago I read a short description of a meal carried to infantry troops on the line by Korean laborers. The fidelity of the description to my own experience caused a shock of emotion and recognition that eclipsed any ever produced by Stephen Crane, Norman Mailer, James Jones, Private Hargrove, or Ernest the Important.

That emotion has been the justification for my production of a novel telling the story of my experiences of a portion of the Korean War as literally and truthfully as possible by 1/18000th of a National Guard Infantry Division.

This book happened and I'm very pleased to have written it.

Sincerely,

Thomas F. MacLean

The Second Casualty

George Orwell wrote that the first casualty in war is truth.

I. In which the historical context of the novel is set in an address to the editor and readers. The author describes his hopes for the book. Incidents from high school, the details of his mother's illness and Tom's enlistment in the National Guard.

II. More high school incidents, the mobilization of the National Guard. Tom's anxiety lest he be excluded from the experience because he is underage. His escape from home into the army.

III. An August troop train from Oklahoma to Louisiana. Introduction to Camp Polk.

IV. Camp meals and routine, the joys of the PX, troop instruction and recreation. How to police an area to clean it of cigarette butts.

V. First pass off the post to a soldier town and soldier bars. Description of letter writers, KP, drinking and gambling.

VI. The band company. Tom's first whore, a belle of Shreveport. Introduction to gas masks, grenades, aptitude tests, and the menace of venereal disease.

VII. The governor of Oklahoma visits Camp Polk. A trip to an Opelousas, Louisiana, whorehouse to see a woman with enormous breasts.

VIII. A trip to Beaumont, Texas. The NKPA on the run. A band detail plays with/for a visiting circus at Camp Polk.

IX. The suicide of Tom's mother. Return to Oklahoma for the funeral. Tom's younger brother writes the details.

X. Winter at Camp Polk. The Chinese enter the war. A trip to Lake Charles. Two whorehouses in Port Arthur, Texas.

XI. We learn the division is to go to Japan. A nostalgic visit by the CG of the 3rd Division.

XII. New Year's in Oklahoma City. The band plays for the embarcation of the division at New Orleans. Troop ship life on the Caribbean.

XIII. Transiting the Panama Canal. North to San Francisco,

across the Pacific to Hokkaido. Camp life and training in Japan.

XIV. Off the post. Street scenes and whorehouses in Sapporo.

XV. Toshiko. Bivouac. A visit to a Japanese mountain spa. Tom imagines his suicide in his mind's eye.

XVI. Tom's rest and recreation leave to southern Japan. A week at Atami.

XVII. Amphibious training, An invitation to domesticity. The band tour to Tokyo, the Peace Treaty concert, the excursion to Lake Shikotsu. Rumors of assignment of the division to Korea.

XVIII. The move to winter quarters. A trip to Otaru. The departure via Navy attack transport to Korea.

XIX. By landing craft to Inchon. Impressions of the replacement depot at Yongdungpo, Seoul, and begging children. By truck to the division supply route railhead. What bandsmen do in Korea.

XX. Righting an injustice at the division IG. Duty with the Division Headquarters defense platoon. Tom transfers out of the band company. Souvenir collecting, a trip to the rear area. Tom meets General Ridgeway.

XXI. An alert in the hills above division headquarters. An accident involving a phosphorous grenade. Visits by the USO. Tom's first shower in five months. The farewell party. Chorwon to Pusan via train. Pusan to Sasebo by ferry. Tom is discouraged from re-enlisting in Japan.

XXII. By troopship to Fort Mason, San Francisco and by ferry to Camp Stoneman, Pittsburg, California. Processing for discharge and further troop education. Via train to Ft. Sill, Oklahoma. A pass to Oklahoma City where Tom presents himself to his grandmother and reacquaints himself with downtown. He goes to the movies.

CHAPTER 1

THE 2ND CASUALTY

1950. The massive, ignorant populations of the East and West are poised to clash by night, by day. Flickering dischromatic newsreel symbols of man's ability to produce even greater chaos and suffering from the exhausted disorder of the unresolved suspicions and the venal self-interests left over from Worldly War II. Statesmen and international thugs, Running Dogs and Fat Cats, and the commentators thereon are poised and posturing their personae for the dramatic days to come. Drum-da-rum, underneath rum-a-humma-rumma-humma, and so on.

Kim Ii Sung, Stalin, and Harry Truman urge and are urged, plans emerge for the massive movements of men and their equipment kilorearns of orders and other paperwork that will direct and control the behavior of the as yet sleeping, working, day-dreaming, lusting members of the human race metastisize.

Here is the story of Tom, an integer, a cipher, an atom of that vast chemical equation of War, Peace, and Human Experience.

Actually, the foregoing may be just a bit unfair to Kim Ii Sung and the other aged and mostly, by now deceased, creatures of venal and nationalistic self-interest.

History is going to happen after all. There will be events. If someone has to do it, it might as well be Joe or Harry. Absolutely no hard feelings. We think we understand, we really do. Those events, those ignorant armies. I believe it's something like descending a sandy slope. One does decide to take the initial step, but then how much of the downward progress is under control? The movement of the sand itself assists and even requires the completion of the descent.

The contracting metaphor of climbing a sandy slops requires an altogether different perspective of the events of 1950. Who will write that story?

At any rate, my sandy friends, no ill will. If the stage were not the Korean Peninsula, it could have as well been southeast Asia, or Central America, or Iran, or Gettysburg, PA. I believe that's fair enough. We'll leave the assessment of blame, if any, at that.

Something hundred hours, 7 JUN 1950: What I Did On My Summer Vacation. Or, The Story Of My Life 1949-1952. Three Years Before The Rest. The Groupies Of Wrath. The 2nd Casualty.

I, Thomas F. MacLean, aged 46, being of sound mind and motivated by hopes of achieving wealth, an estate; or, at least, to net out $100,000 after taxes and the deduction of my share of promotional expenses, do hereby undertake to combine a few notes, some anecdotes, into paragraphs or vignettes to result in an autobiographical first novel suitable for serialization; for paperback sales of millions; and for the cinema.

I am, of course, willing to let a scrupulous editor work his/her will upon the material. I'm not kidding. There is a market demand for this kind of book. Really, any book. Why else are there publishing houses, printers, manufacturers of ink, paper, and wire book racks. There are reviewers, idle hours to be filled on lunch breaks and commuter trains. There are public libraries whose old books wear out, teen-agers off for the summer to be employed checking out books. Let the above be my justification, my quest, my fulfillment.

First, though, some fantasies of economic success. A modest house on Beacon Hill, to enjoy within a minute's walk in season, caroling on Louisburg Square. This as a reward to my wife who lived in Boston as a child. Another home on the upper slope of a hill in San Francisco, or San Diego, or some other city blessed with a salubrious clime. The minimum fantasy, the best/worst case, a modestly generous supplement to my public school teacher income which could; alas, terminate because of deficiencies in the teacher negotiated contract, or declining enrollment, or as the consequence of some misfired personal professional endeavor.

The form of the novel is of interest to the professional reader. It should be clear by what follows that I have chosen to write a musing letter to myself.

5505 Colorado Drive

Concord, CA 94521

June 17, 1979

Dear Tom,

This is the form I use comfortably in letters to my friends which could as easily be letters to myself. They are a mixture of whimsy, humorous comments on current events, references to past experiences.

Love,

Tom

I have also a keen affection for the structure, the sturdy scaffolding of <u>Tom Jones</u>. The author's comments on the progress of the story are so helpful. I'm a fan of Gunter Grass whose Flounder contemporizes the past, among many other accomplishments. And, there's Jose Cela whose units of drama told the grim story so well. And, I have my own experiences, bizarre, terrible, and funny, buried somewhere in my head and notes that concretize somewhat on their own. The author as frescoer who smears and limns the images around until the plaster hardens.

My narrative will begin with the events of my life a bit less than a year prior to the onset of the Korean War, that is, the time of the beginning of the Junior year in high school and will cover the circumstances of the new school, the mixed chorus, the tenor saxophone, the whistling sibilance of the biology teacher's articulation, the attempts on the lives of my younger brother and me by our mother, the recurrence of her mental illness, the National Guard, the induction physical with my concern about the lack of armpit hair, the train, Camp Polk, the urinals, the PX, the CO_2 pistols, the circus, Shreveport, De Ridder, Leesville, Whiskey Sours, Tom Collinses, the front porch, Texas, hitchhiking, Jeannine, the suicide, the Red Cross, Camp LeRoy Johnson, New Orleans, oysters, troop ships, Japan, hand—jobs and massages, more trains, ferry boats, Atami, and Korea, assault transports, Inchon, trucks, digging in, cold, guard duty, garbage, tents, ammo, bodies, flares, searchlights, hunger, barbed wire, officers, General Ridgeway, booby-traps, replacement companies, Marines, Camp Stoneman, and discharge to civilian status perchance to work as a spot-welder in a potato chip sales rack manufacturing factory.

Now, toward the end of relating all of this, I will be totally honest when able, and fabricate what I wish, and embroider imaginatively when I wish and produce reams of copy. Since I have little desire to separate wheat from chaff and would probably have less success in identifying chaff than a competent and willing editor, I will transcribe it all for you and for me.

Would it be helpful, I wonder, to use some shorthand identifier to distinguish at a glance what I consider fact, embroidery, or fiction? This little book of myth and history. Perhaps a miniature marginal butterfly to identify flights of fancy. Should the butterfly introduce the passage or appear at the end? I might use some sort of catch phrase if its repetition proved not too irritating; this is it, or, this happened. I don't think italics or Gothic script would work. Maybe an asterisk could be used to indicate the germs of simple fact. After pausing to consider this, I've pretty much decided against any of it.

Just a note to the down-line processor. In the event I am unable, through illness or death to accede personally, go ahead, garble any message and trivialize any story. Or, mush what truth and art might have been created to meet the specific needs of print that week or film that season. Just produce money. At least the first time around. Oh! Ye who commercialize, commercialize away with this author's blessing. I'll do with words what I felt I couldn't do with sketches, or career choice, and write for the money to provide myself with an elemental buffer to the anxiety that those of us aged 46 suddenly feel vulnerable to, to provide myself with a thin defense against old man's poverty.

You see, I would exercise my wit and experience and lack of shrewdness on paper rather than as an elderly new boy in some retail or white collar endeavor. The gentleman here would like to return this can of paint. Is there some key I push now on the register, or how do I do that? Maybe I can get back to you on that after I check with my 17-year-old supervisor.

So, there with the summer ahead and pencil and paper

I began. This time with my goal in mind and stated. Not fame, glory, recognition, adulation. But a check, or better, a series of checks to invest in real property and a regulated lifestyle of dignity, combining work with extended periods of recreation. Gradually easing into a quiet round of leisure activities. After a suitable interval I could respond to my publisher's accountants to write about my years of elementary school teaching, or the 10 years between Korea and my marriage.

A delicately visaged male youth of 15 with ample rear bulging in new blue jeans, shod in penny loafers, walks rapidly up then down a crowded corridor lined with grey metal lockers and excited high school students. It is Tom's first day at the new school. He looks for the chorus room. He knows the bell is to ring soon. Perhaps he is looking for the room designated as his homeroom. The directions of the school secretary, so clear in the office, bear no relation to the architecture of the unfamiliar building.

Why is he, Tom, a high school Junior, here at a new school rather than returning to greet his old classmates? To pick up where they had left off the previous spring? To play out the roles assumed, or imposed, by the wealth of their parents and the other threads that make up their juvenile tapestries?

Tom was here because his mother, a teacher, after a mental breakdown and attempted suicide, has emerged from the state hospital to begin a new job at a high school in another community. Not at the school Tom is to attend, but in a neighboring community.

Tom's heavily oiled curly hair and the pack of Chesterfields in the pocket of his white short-sleeved shirt exist as efforts to conceal Tom's anxious anxiety that he does appear younger than he really is, a young, high school Junior. Rose Oil, a hair grooming product colored a passionate carmine had been applied in perfumy profusion. That was sartorially correct. The cigarettes, a habit assiduously pursued had exerted their addiction only weeks before after a whole summer and a bit more before spent in seeking to acquire the cachet of maturity derived from the pangs of nicotine dependency. All adult males smoke cigarettes. At age 15 Tom had achieved this level of sophisticated manful addiction a full year, or a year-and-a-half earlier than most of his peers. He rejoiced in his ability to draw the smoke deep into his lungs without gagging or nausea.

Tom charged the cigarettes to his mother's grocery account. The grocer, who saw little of her, assumed Tom's mother was the smoker. It was the practice of discreet female teachers even in the late 1940's to confine their smoking to their homes, and they would, of course, not smoke while shopping for groceries. No well-bred person would. It was such a confirmed part of Tom's routine to obtain his cigarettes in this way that he was really taken aback not too long before the end by the intensity of his mother's unhappiness when she confronted him with the tobacco crumbs she had discovered in his shirt pocket. He had assumed that if she were to find out it would be from the tags in the grocer's charge book right there with the lettuce, coffee, Jello, and other staves of life. His mother wept, first angrily and then helplessly, for what seemed to Tom a long time and to his confusion blamed herself for his smoking.

So, here is yet another new school. In the 1940's his family had moved frequently joining in the nervous dislocations of the war. Tom had attended 13 schools the first eight grades. He developed a new school routine he'd used with some success or at least used until the small groups of children he joined continued rather than terminated their games or conversations to gaze at him. Initially he'd be rather quiet and well-mannered to get the favorable attention of the teachers. His school work was usually adequate. Later he could be quietly show-offish in a good natured way that wasn't too disruptive or threatening to the teachers' authority, if it was he'd quickly back off, to win some attention from his classmates.

I am sitting on a dias carpeted in a rust berber. My elbows rest easily on the arms of the chair, my hands are folded lightly in my lap.

The cameras swing their snouts toward me. The host asks, "Why did you kill your mother and your little brother, you greasy piece of scum?" The questioner knows why, of course. All of them do. It is because I am a cowardly, selfish, rabbitty piece of vermin.

I answer, "I didn't want to, but to be perfectly honest, a wish to survive seized me and carried me away from their sinking ship."

A member of the television studio audience bent her neck at an awkward angle as the show host pushed a microphone at her mouth. She said, "I just want to say, you make me want to puke, you worthless piece of slime."

I nodded acknowledgement of her comment and responded, "It's not all over. In a previous existence I was Pearly McLean, Shirley Mulayn, Curly Furlain, Billy Spolain, and so on. It isn't over again."

The red light snapped off, the technicians coiled their lines, the audience filed out. I didn't even see the show host leave for lunch. I left through the same door as the audience. My agent and my publisher had assured me this is how to sell my book.

I walked home from the interview. Halfway between the studio and my home two men in business suits stepped in front of me, flashed their ID badges and put me in the backseat of a Plymouth sedan with state license plates. I was driven just outside town to the State Prison School for Cowardly, Depraved Adolescents. There was a long drive up from the highway to a brick building with bars on many of the windows. A pimply-faced trustee followed a lawn mower around a wide breadth of Bermuda grass lawn.

I began to anticipate the possibility of physical pain. Maybe the internment process involved dental probing and/or inoculations. But, if they wanted to lock me in solitary, that was just fine with me. I could be a model prisoner.

At the previous school Tom played saxophone in the marching and pep bands. With the school secretary's encouragement, he enrolled in Band and Chorus. Such a fine way to meet a good group of kids. He looked for the band room to introduce himself to the teacher before school. Perhaps he should find the homeroom and report in first. He realized he hadn't listened to the secretary's directions. He'd been occupied rather with attempting to appear attentive.

The bell rings, the corridor clears, and Tom still has no idea where he is supposed to be. The white slip on which his schedule has been written comes to mind. He'd stuck it in his pocket. It says Home Rm. Mrs. Bradley, Rm. 104. He finds the room. Everyone is seated listening to a small, trim, grey-haired woman in a knit dress. Tom enters the room and takes an awkward seat in a student desk in the first row.

Mrs. Bradley was calling the roll from a stack of pink cards. Tom's name is called, and as a stranger in this small and friendly community, he is asked to stand and tell something of himself and his family. He is less conscious of the class than of the girl seated next to him. She is wearing a cotton house-dress and smells of laundry soap and starchy fresh ironing. You're country enough, Tom thinks. I'll bet one of your grandmothers has a goiter. A grandmother you might see in downtown Talequah on a Saturday morning in town for the day. She has this huge goiter thing on one side of her neck and lower. This girl probably has cousins in Texas with orange front teeth. As a matter of fact. Tommy, unknown to him, I have a great uncle who's a Federal Court of Appeals judge in New York City. Well, has he seen your starched flour sack dress and fuzzy legs?

All morning Tom carries his notebooks and sack lunch because there was no time to assign him a locker. Carrying the stuff around was awkward and troublesome. At noon he was relieved to obtain a locker assignment so he could store some of his things. He ate his lunch alone seated on the steps at one side of the building, and then walked a couple of blocks off campus to smoke a cigarette.

In the early afternoon Tom is called out of Biology class to the principal's office and told of a report telephoned to the school that someone saw him smoking a cigarette off campus, and that smoking is against school rules. Tom is astonished. He can conceive of no other reaction than total indifference of anyone, other than his mother, to his smoking. Why would anyone give the incident a second thought much less report it to the school? But an elderly woman had seen a juvenile lounging near her home and had provided the school with his description. If Tom wished to get off to a good start here at Bethany High, and if he wished to avoid further action he was to refrain from smoking. And it was injurious to his health as well. Welcome to our small town.

After supper Tom carefully scanned his mother's behavior to detect any depression or signs of illness, much as a small boat sailor cocks an eye to the weather to detect any sky symptoms of change that might endanger him. He noticed nothing amiss and afterwards at the kitchen sink washed the remains of the Kraft Dinner, canned corn, and chocolate pudding off the plates his ten-year-old brother was to dry and put back into the cabinet.

Tom writes up some things for homework. In response to a frequent request, he gives his mother a backrub. He listens to the radio in bed and then sleeps.

In the morning he is relieved to hear his mother out of bed and in the kitchen running water, making coffee. If she is out of bed and active things will be all right for one more day.

Now, would it not be strange if the recording of these ancient anxieties would provide the security so long lacking. Insecurity. Checking every morning for a year to see if your mother, your provider, your breadwinner, were able to face the day, or if she would remain abed, ill. The newspaper today relates the story of a writer of mystery adventure who was able to quit work at age 60 and live by writing. Oh, dream! oh, life. Be my tax shelter, tax free annuity, income property, Dear Pencil.

Tom was to make friends easily at the new school. Tom continued to sit next to the girl who wears starched dresses. She is nice. She is to marry a classmate after high school graduation. Tom meets her best-friend whose housedresses are almost as starched, who smells almost as intensely of soap, who also has downy legs. Tom walks this girl home from school from time to time. He listens to her talk about her family, her opinions of movies, her experiences at school. She calls him at home in the late afternoon. At the appropriate time his attentiveness is rewarded with kisses.

Tom is marking time. In less than two years he will be old enough to join the Navy although from time to time he leans toward the Air Force. He has looked forward to military service since childhood. He always enjoyed playing soldier more than cowboys. World War II, the weekly picture show, magazines, bus and train stations filled with young men in uniform, heroism, action, romance. And it looked better and better. He has a closet full of gear he'd bought at the local war surplus stores. Entrenching tools, C rations, helmet liner, webbed belt, canteen, a practice bayonet with a black plastic blade. In elementary school he'd carried his lunch to school in a metal ammo box.

The high school music teacher is a veteran of the war and a warrant officer in the National Guard. He is the CO of the Division Band that drills in Oklahoma City. A half-dozen or so of the high school band members have joined the Guard for the money and experiences.

A classmate offers to drive him to a Thursday meeting night at the Armory. Listening to the adventures on the weekends at various training sites and the two weeks at Ft. Sill, Tom laments that he is only 15, 16 the end of November.

His age is no problem. No proof of age is required. Thursday evening, he drives to the Armory with a carload of classmates dressed in fatigues. He watches their drill on the Armory floor and goes with his friend to the personnel sergeant seated at a typewriter who signs him up. When asked his age Tom says he is 15. The sergeant says quietly that we'll have to make that 18. He was even issued a uniform that evening, was assigned a locker, and left with his friends at 10 exulting in his good fortune, feeling grown up and manly.

Next Thursday evening after additional paperwork, Tom was directed to the offices of the medical unit and barring complications of the blood and urine tests Tom was pronounced not only free of hernias but fit in every way for service.

The next weekend was the glorious matriculation from childhood to youth. Early Saturday morning the Band Company was convoyed to a rifle range some 20 miles from the city. Tom was dressed in fatigues, talking to his friends and enjoying the view from the bench of the truck.

At the range he was detailed to service in a great concrete trench to pull, mark, and paste targets that were fired upon from some hundreds of yards away by men qualifying on carbines and M1s.

There is the satisfying routine of waving signal flags as the work proceeds to ready the right, the left, and the firing line. There is the excitement of rounds cracking through the paper targets overhead. The hoisting of disks on poles to indicate where the rounds had entered the target and Maggie's drawers, the flag waved for those rounds that missed the target altogether.

That afternoon Tom was instructed on the firing line. He learns how to twist the leather sling of the M1 to steady the rifle. He experiences the awkward pull on his arm and shoulder muscles as he pushes his left elbow under the weapon and raises his right elbow. He sees the results of a neighbor's failure to mind the location of his right thumb that the recoil pushes into his eye. Tom was given Kotex to tuck into his shirt sleeve to cushion his left elbow when firing prone.

Tom zeros in and raises the sights a click or two and twists the windage knob to compensate for the cluster of rounds in the lower right of the target. He is immensely pleased at the end to learn he has qualified on the M1. He is a marksman. He will receive a metal badge to wear on the pocket of his blouse.

This is the day Tom learns which is his gun and which is his piece. It rains and he sits in the rain cleaning the weapon, pushing oily patches up and down the barrel, and feeling in every way a soldier and glad of it.

CHAPTER 2

Monday at school Tom decides his Biology teacher is the worst case. In 1949 not a whole lot of people want to teach high school science in a small town in Oklahoma. Tom did not know this man's story. Supposedly, he had been a teacher somewhere quite a while ago, and then he either went into business or had a fairly decent job of some kind during the war; and now, years later he'd become a teacher again. At any rate, this was the man's first year in the classroom in a long time. He was in his late 40's or early 50's. He had neatly combed and parted dark hair. He wore rather good suits but seemed to favor a light green whipcord. Like many male teachers he leaned against the chalkboard and dusted himself up. He wore a clean heavily starched white shirt. A handkerchief in his coat pocket. He was clean shaven. He had a sort of raw-boned country look. His manner was mild and bland, faintly pleasant but very reserved. Again, he was supposed to have some sort of science background, but he never alluded to it. He said, or discussed, nothing on the subject of Biology that could not be found in the textbook, which they read in 10-page increments for homework, and then discussed in class by answering questions when called upon.

Perhaps it was the limitations. A room, student desks, and textbooks only. No charts or posters. Perhaps it was a limited imagination. But it was a reading and discussion class. Biology, like History or English. Never a specimen in a jar, a tray with dissecting knives, an allusion to the cicadas whirring outside in the elm trees that shaded that side of the building.

But what made the class well-nigh unbearable was a speech impediment the teacher suffered. I don't know, but suspect, it was caused by dentures. It was a sharp whistling sibilance, a long incessant whistle that accompanied the production of any /s/ sound. It was startling in its effect. It overshadowed any other impression of the man, or of the pathetic lessons, he plodded through each day. Loud, persistent, inevitable, intrusive, the whistle produced by each /s/ was beyond humor or novelty, compassion or resentment, or acceptance, or even notoriety. In the classroom it precipitated no giggles or knowing looks. It failed to create a bond with the classmates born of shared experience. The whistle was just there, too apparent and demanding of attention to go away. Tom made a B in Biology.

The weekly National Guard meetings the school year of 1949- 1950 gave the only real structure to Tom's disorderly world. They provided the only real pleasure or recreation.

Tom's mother became ill again. School was a repetition of almost every class he'd had since the eighth grade. There were no math or lab classes. He did learn to type. But the Guard was interesting, even fascinating. He enjoyed the drills. He was eager to learn to obey, to stand guard, to salute. He enjoyed sorting things and cleaning weapons, riding around in vehicles. He looked forward to becoming 17. He'd decided to join the Air Force. Several older classmates had done just that. They had quit school, they hung around town for several weeks waiting to go to Lackland in Texas for training. One boy in an excess of enthusiasm had his service number tattooed on his forearm.

Tom didn't attend school regularly. Sometimes he would go in the morning for the music and English classes and cut loose in the afternoon. His mother often spent the day, or several days, in bed unable to function. He feared her further attempts at suicide, but didn't know whom to tell, or how even to protect himself. He was able to get money from her, or took a few dollars from her purse, and would walk several miles to a roadside tavern which for some unfathomable reason sold, risking its license, beer to teen-agers. There Tom could get drunk.

Some nights at a bait stand near the tavern Tom sold minnows to fishermen, night fishing, who would ring a bell to awaken him. The minnows sold by the dozen. Tom would dip into the large open galvanized tanks and count them out into the two-piece minnow buckets, and then wash his hands to rid them of the rank, strong, fishy, weedy-water smell. The owner of the stand paid Tom in homemade wine, or a jar of white lightning; or, rarely, a few dollars and the cot in the minnow shack.

Several times that winter Tom finds his mother lying on the cold grate of the floor furnace with heavy blankets over her body. She hasn't turned on the gas. He attempts to carry her, or bully her, into returning to bed. Or, if there is time into getting dressed and going to work.

Tom dresses and might go to school, or he will walk to town, catch a bus to the city where he will walk and window shop, or go to a picture show.

Tom's main interest is the coming summer encampment of the National Guard at Fort Sill. He will have at least two weeks of full-time military life. He can volunteer for advance and rear guards, and perhaps get four or more days of service. He'll have Army chow and drink beer at the PX and buy cigarettes for a dollar a carton. He'll earn close to $100. In the course of the months, Tom received promotions and by spring was a corporal and earned a little over $7 a drill.

The school year was over the end of May. Tom sat around friends' houses in the hot afternoon. When it cooled off in the evening, they drove in carloads to drive-ins for beer and barbecued beef sandwiches, and spent hours speculating about the receptivity to a direct sexual approach of several of the girls at school, about whether cock was properly used in reference to male or female genitals, and about travel in the service and the attendant access to sexual adventures in the whorehouses of the world, wherever the U.S. military was stationed.

It was but a few days before the Guard was to convoy to Fort Sill that Tom was telephoned by a friend with the incredible report that the Guard was being mobilized into Federal service because of the crossing of the 38th Parallel by the North Koreans. He was shaking with excitement. His classmates telephoned back and forth with the current status of negotiations, arguments, and discussions with their parents for permission to accompany the Division to Louisiana for training and where the Division would receive inductees to bring it to full strength.

Tom was the youngest of his group and felt he had the largest job to persuade his mother not to interfere. He had to gain the acquiescence of the CO who also knew his age. The other youths had their own battles to win. Some parents objected to their sons missing the Senior year of high school. Others feared the effect of the military experience on a 17-year-old.

The men and boys of the Band Company reported for duty at the Armory every day now. The men made arrangements with their employers and their families. Some obtained discharges because of age or responsibilities.

There was not much to do at the Armory. The supply and personnel sergeants were the busiest. There was roll call in the morning and inspections. There was some packing of equipment but most of the Guardsmen were told to stay out of the way. Some were assigned guard posts of a sort and hung around the corners of the buildings trying to find some shade. There was some close order drill. They were given vouchers good for a sandwich and a cold drink for lunch at a nearby drive-in.

One night the American Legion had a buffet with cold cuts and beer to say good-bye to the Division. The driver of the car Tom came with had a hard time finding a parking place. There were lots of cars. Several hundred Guardsmen crowded into an upstairs meeting room and ate, and drank self-consciously acknowledging the best wishes of the Legionnaires.

The departure of the Division was in all the Oklahoma newspapers. Each town of any size had a Guard unit or two consisting of high-schoolers and some veterans. The rumor was the Division was to be brought to full strength and sent to Germany for garrison duty. Tom grew wild with anxiety when the thought of any interference with his participation in the adventure might arise. His mother continued ill and quietly disapproving. She said she didn't want him to go, but to this point she had done nothing to interfere with the process.

Another medical examination went smoothly enough although Tom was acutely ashamed of the lack of hair yet developing on his chest or under his arms. In response to a final interview question: Do you want to go with the Division? Tom answered so forcibly in the affirmative: Yes, sir; yes, sir; indeed, sir, that the examiner smiled and said, "Well then, you're on your way." It was better than a birthday, it was better than Christmas, than the last day of school. He almost cried, he could scarcely keep from skipping and laughing triumphantly out loud. He was free now and secure. He'd have a job and uniforms and adventures. He wouldn't be an anxious dependent and a frightened eye-witness anymore to what was happening to his mother. And when the worst happened, when it did, he would be far away and wouldn't see it, or participate in it, or perish. Tom surrendered his mother, and his little brother that he not perish, but have life.

CHAPTER 3

This resolution of Tom's problem had required the intervention of the Korean War. North Korean tank battalions routed South Korean defense forces. Sleepy, unhappy Americans, occupation troops, were ferried from Japan to die in the dusty hills south of Seoul and Taejon. Even civilians were sacrificed to preserve Tom's life. The aged Syngman Rhee expended energy on Tom's behalf supported by the heroic ministrations of his American wife. The dispatches of Ambassador Muccio. The meetings of the Joint Chiefs of Staff. Tom's little problem required these responses. A necessarily incomplete list of thank yous to the ROK 12th Regiment, the men and boys of Companies B and C, 1st Bn, 21st Inf Regt, 24th Inf Div.

Why not just the quiet intervention of an alert neighbor with a word to the right social agency? No, it was as when a sea creature spews millions of cells into the sea to give the few a chance at maturity. Tom's little problem required the ejaculation of millions of solutions on the off chance that one would save him. Thank you, General MacArthur.

One evening before he left, Tom's mother said that earlier in the week she had telephoned the CO and he had reassured her that he would look out for the local high school boys, and then she had telephoned some colonel who had told her the Division would probably not leave the United States.

Tom was shaken by the initiative his mother had taken and the power the poor sick woman still had. Merely with a phone call or a note, she could have interrupted his adventure. But she released him. He felt no gratitude, only profound relief.

The Band Company was to entrain early in the morning. The gear was all secured. Enormous crates made of yellow pine boards had been lifted onto trucks and sent on ahead. The rooms at the Armory were empty, swept and mopped. The Company had said good-bye to family and friends, who now returned to their homes or jobs, and was now restricted to the motor pool.

Tom had said good-bye to his mother and little brother. He had eaten no breakfast in his haste to accomplish the departure, and now in the early afternoon he was hot, thirsty for something cold to drink, and hungry.

There was absolutely no word from anyone why they hadn't left, or when they might leave.

They waited all day. Roll call had been at 7:00 in the morning. There was some concern about a missed lunch, but there was no real grumbling. Everyone was too excited and looking forward to the departure. Someone said the CO and several senior non-coms had taken a jeep and had their lunch at an air-conditioned restaurant, but even that rumor caused little resentment as there was more curiosity about coming events that would directly affect them.

About 8:30 that evening a jeep appeared with box lunches from a fried chicken restaurant. They were handed round. Each box contained two pieces of fried chicken, a covered paper cup of cole slaw, a roll, a napkin and a wooden fork. The food was eaten in moments and before the after dinner cigarettes were smoked the order was given to get onto the trucks.

The Company was driven in a few minutes to the rail head. The troops boarded the chair cars with their duffel bags, and weapons, and a short time later the train moved forward. Half of the men and boys were asleep before the lights of Oklahoma City were left behind.

But, Tom was awake, determined to relish every moment of being a soldier. The men and boys had dispersed themselves throughout the car. They lay in the aisles and climbed into the overhead luggage racks. There was a complete jumble of men, field packs, duffel bags, and weapons. The only illumination was a dull yellowish light near the water fountain and toilets at the end of the car.

The paper cups went first, then the water was finished. It was a cool moist night, only an occasional farm light, or an auto with its lights pacing the train. Tom went to sleep sitting up, his head cushioned against a field pack wedged between his seatmate and himself.

Tom awoke when it was quite light. His clothing was stale and wet with sweat. He was headachy from the heat and smoke. His arms, and legs, and back ached. His feet in the unlaced boots felt hot and swollen. He wanted to wash his face and get a drink of water, the other soldiers told him the wash basin and water fountain were dry. His canteen was empty.

Tom wondered when and how they'd be fed. Other soldiers volunteered what they'd order for breakfast next chance in a restaurant or at home. Most began with a tall glass of ice cold orange juice.

Tom really did feel bad, almost ill. The train stopped somewhere in the country. The breeze generated by the moving train stopped. The car began to bake. Some proposed they jump out on the track to scout for water, or information; or, best of all, a country store with a metal boxful of ice and cold soda pop. Cigarettes were giving out and those soldiers with cigarettes became less and less willing to supply the others. Matches were at a premium too, and each match served four or five. No one walked by the car along the tracks. The soldiers leaned out of the windows and shouted questions or obscene comments about the situation to soldiers leaning from adjacent cars.

Once a brakeman walked near a car toward the rear of the train and returned to the caboose to the yells, threats, and queries of the troops. Some of the soldiers began to half convince themselves they were ready to jump off the train and hitch hike home.

The train lurched forward again in shuddering crashes and seemed now to fly, as if to make up time, through country which became quite novel and unfamiliar compared to the rolling farmland and wooded bottom land around Oklahoma City.

There were piney woods and stretches of raised track

bed that went above snakey-looking creeks, or flooded areas growing with tall trees encumbered with hanging mosses. The humidity increased as well as the heat, and the men hung up blankets on the sunny side of the train that whipped and snapped in the steaming wind. There was some real distress as the men sat now quiet and miserable, sweat plastering their hair to their foreheads. The sergeants refused them permission to take off their fatigue jackets.

Everything in the car now was grimy from the soot and bits of cinder thrown in the windows by the hot heavy wind.

The occasional small towns appeared deserted. The train rocketed past the stations with the raised platforms of the baggage depots. The empty baggage wagons stood on their enormous iron wheels. The fields and woods were deserted under the oppressive midday heat.

About four o'clock in the afternoon the train slowed perceptibly and moved into an area of scattered yellow one- and two-story frame buildings. There was a contagious interest as the soldiers roused themselves and word passed from person-to-person and then down the cars that this must be Camp Polk.

The men and boys sat up or moved from one side of the car to the other to look with intensity at what their situation was to be. The buildings appeared unused, vacant, neglected. The paint was blistered and peeling. Waist-high clumps of weeds grew from the sandy soil and intruded into the cracked roadways. There were cattle huddled in the shade of the buildings.

The train now slowed to a few miles an hour, stopped, and then the men searched out their own packs, and weapons, and duffel bags, and buckled on web belts and laced and buckled their boots. Tom's car stopped in front of a warehouse with an open door and one or two military vehicles and nondescript pickups parked outside. A half dozen civilians dressed in work clothes sat on packing boxes in the shade of the door and quietly regarded the train.

A sergeant appeared at one end of the car and ordered the soldiers to vacate the car, to fall-in in the street alongside the train. There was a tremendous rush of crowding to comply and leave the car. A civilian train conductor in a blue suit stood by the step and urged the heavily loaded men to watch their step down.

Tom saw the CO standing over in the shaded doorway as he and the rest of the company struggled to organize themselves for roll call and inspection with much dressing of ranks and fussy right-facing and left-facing and taking one or two steps forward. This in the full heat of the afternoon and laden with full field packs, duffel bags, and weapons.

Roll was called, the first sergeant declared the company ready for inspection, all present or accounted for, and the CO detached himself from the shade and strode through and around the rectangular group of men, occasionally inspecting a weapon or commenting on an unbuttoned pocket or collar gone awry.

This accomplished the CO returned to face the company now standing at parade rest and announced that they were indeed at Camp Polk, that they were to march to their company area to draw bedding and other gear. That they would be fed an evening meal and afterwards they could shower and rest. That they were restricted to the barracks, but that PX privileges would be allowed soon.

The effect of so much information gave a sense of purpose again to the experience, and when the Company was right-faced and marched to a cadence, the Bandsmen had a feeling that the difficulties of travel were over and the glamor, and novelty and adventure could begin anew.

The heavily loaded men and boys were unable to maintain the cadence counted by the sergeant. The troops attempted to shift the burdens of duffel bags and weapons from one arm or shoulder to the other. The field pack straps bit deeper into the shoulders and arms numbing them. The soldiers dragging duffels on the ground were shouted at and told to pick them up and carry them. The order for route step was finally given.

It took the Company over an hour to make the three mile distance. By that time the men's fatigue jackets were soaked with sweat, with faint salty lines at the edge of the moisture. The faces of the soldiers were beet-red or a pale greenish white. The suffering indifferent Band Company achieved the Company street outside their two-story barracks. The CO's jeep was parked in the shade of the building containing the supply room and office.

The Company was permitted to fall out and seek the shade and water of the barracks. The hottest part of the day was over now, and the shade was plentiful on the east side of the buildings. Some of the soldiers began joking, began speculating on the probable locations of air-conditioned post theaters and quite seriously boasting of the number of hamburgers and bottles of beer they'd consume when permitted to go to the PX visible across a field from the Company area.

After a half-hour's rest the men were told to carry their equipment into the barracks and then to line up for the evening meal at the mess hall some three or four buildings over. They took their mess kits and canteen cups all clanging with one mess kit half attached by a loop of metal to the handle of the other half, the canteen cup hanging also by a slot in its handle, the spoon, fork, and knife likewise. The noisy line of soldiers inched its way into the mess hall.

The two halves of the mess kit were detached and held in the middle by the left hand and held up to the serving line. Two slices of bread, two slices of bologna, two slices of processed cheese, canned corn, Jello with mixed fruit, and a dipper of iced tea into the canteen cup.

The mess hall was a low one-story rectangular building about a third of which was taken up with a kitchen and storage area. The rest of the building was a single room provided with wooden tables and benches down either side under the windows.

The first table on the left upon entering was the

sergeants' table. They were from time to time joined by an officer or two. This was always the most cheerful group with hearty, manly chaffing and comradery the customary behavior. It was at this table the CO's stories were punctuated by respectful guffaws. At this table they ate from trays. The diners would call on the KP's for additional meat or drink, or special condiments from the cook's store, pickles, sauces, or double desserts.

At this first meal the grousing and complaining about Army food began, but Tom didn't complain and was only mildly curious about future meals, especially the quantity of them as he finished his portion and saw no more forthcoming.

Two large garbage cans containing immersion heaters were just beyond the exit steps of the mess hall. The first held soapy water; the second, hot rinse water. The mess gear was again attached into its clanging lump and sloshed vigorously up and down in both waters and then swung around until dry.

The men strolled back to the Company area, some planning surreptitious scouting parties to investigate the post in the event the lack of tobacco and the lure of cold beer provided sufficient incentive.

Back at the supply room they found a truck loaded with metal Army cots to be unloaded and taken into the barracks. Some men were detailed to clean the latrines of some five years or more of corrosion that had accumulated during the period of disuse since World War II. Other troops were sent back to the mess hall to obtain empty half-gallon food cans which would be filled with water after being nailed to posts in the barracks for use as cigarette butt cans. Other men drew their sheets and pillows.

Footlockers were issued and sergeants stood in the middle of the barracks telling the soldiers how the cots were to be lined up head to foot and spaced so many inches apart. Equipment was dispersed on the open shelves and hanger racks between the barracks windows.

The men and boys were shown how to make up the cots with hospital corners, how to draw the blankets tight. Shouted lists of names interrupted the work every few minutes as soldiers were detailed for fire watch and other housekeeping duties.

Tom was relieved his name was not on the initial KP list of soldiers who would report to the mess hall at 4:30 the next morning.

That talk show host had a hypnotist as a guest this summer. The hypnotist put a woman under and then suggested periods in her life and in that role the hypnotized woman responded to questions about her feelings and attitudes as a 10-year-old, and as a 20-year-old. I wondered how authentic a record I could obtain as a research document for this tale with a tape recording of my own responses to a list of questions and situations I could explore with a hypnotist. There would probably be much more of the immediacy of the 1950's than produced by the undisciplined recall of this pencil scratching from right to left with my sluggish memory attempting to keep two or three words ahead of the mechanics of writing this down.

The Band Company heard the recorded sound of taps but labored on into the night attempting to square things away to the satisfaction of the sergeants. Gradually, the work details accomplished their tasks. The sergeants withdrew to their cots in the squad rooms at the end of the bay, and the lights were extinguished.

CHAPTER 4

At 6:00 AM the duty sergeant turned on the lights and announced formation in 15 minutes in the Company street. The men dressed hurriedly in their fatigues, hastened from the latrine to the formation. The roll was called and PT drill commenced as the morning sun flooded the area. They touched their toes, stretched, rotated their arms, twisted and ran in place. They muttered when told to lie prone in the sand and do push-ups. To make up for this last exercise a senior sergeant concluded their workout with finger flexes and the eyeball glaze. Everyone thought that was funny.

The men were dismissed for breakfast. Some returned to their bunks for another half-hour's sleep, others to shower or shave before the latrines became crowded with latecomers. Others fussed with rearranging their equipment, shining boots, or writing letters home.

At the mess hall there was oatmeal, bacon, canned pears, toast, and coffee. Some few wished to linger over cigarettes and coffee, but were urged out by the KPs who had to rush to scrub the tables, benches, and floor with time to allow them to dry before the noon meal.

Tom caught a glimpse of the other KPs at metal sinks rattling immense piles of pots and pans in steaming wash- and rinse-water.

At the 8:00 AM formation, the Company was detailed into a number of work parties. Some disappeared on trucks, some went to the supply room, others returned to the latrine and barracks to do more scrubbing and polishing.

Many of the sergeants were detailed to instructor school where they were to learn the rudiments of the Army audio visual methods of instruction so common in the introduction of the skills and knowledge deemed necessary to make a soldier function and obey.

Soldiers were detailed to police the Company area picking up trash, raking, field stripping discarded cigarette butts by tearing the paper, scattering the tobacco, and rolling the paper into a small pill to be tossed aside.

As the morning progressed, reports about the PX and other camp facilities began to filter back as soldiers detoured on errands around the camp or took brief leaves from their work parties to check things out. Reports were unanimous that the PX was a great place, a pleasure palace of which they'd dreamed while on the train. Several envied reporters attested to already ingesting a mid-morning Coke and a hamburger. There were cameras and appliances for sale at PX discounts, and cigarettes for $1.50 a carton, candy bars, boxes of detergent, shoe and metal polish; all a soldier could wish for or require, and all transactions attended to by young female clerks.

Tom spent the morning sifting cigarette butts from the sandy soil and in stripping them and pulling weeds and Bermuda grass from the edges of the outside stairs and sidewalks around the Company headquarters.

Tom worked with three or four others under the supervision of the weakest and least-liked sergeant, an unfortunate whose worst bullying instincts were at war with a weaselly wish to ingratiate himself as a way of controlling the detail; who was totally afraid and anxious about the responsibilities of authority that he'd had next to no experience with, but who vainly strutted internally when regarding his sergeant stripes. This sergeant alternated long periods of seeming indifference to whether or not the soldiers did well what he had been charged with the responsibility for seeing that it was done well, with brief intense outbursts where he singled out one men on the detail and attempted to frighten him with sarcasm and invective as an example to the others.

But even the sergeant's worst was only a minor irritant. The last hour before lunch there was so little to do, and the sun so hot that they sat in the shade of a building and smoked cigarettes while the sergeant attempted to regale them with stories of various young women who had pursued him and won his favor. And how he had tricked them into paying for everything and on and on.

The noon meal that day was bologna, processed cheese, Jello, bread, canned corn and iced tea.

The men rushed to return to the barracks where they were allowed in their bunks to rest. There was mail for many. Letters from parents, wives and girlfriends, and the first of packages containing cookies, dried fruit, crackers. Tom lay on his bunk until ordered to formation on the Company street. Blankets on the cots were hurriedly tightened, gear straightened, and in the street the Company was counted off again into work details.

Tom was among 30 or so remaining who were assigned for lack of any specific tasks to close order drill. In the course of the afternoon several miles were traveled up and down the Company street and in one grand circuit of their section of the post. It was hot, but there were short breaks and Tom enjoyed marching anyway. Most of the soldiers were competent marchers so the drill was spent mainly on smooth transitions from oblique and flanking movements, sort of sophisticated stuff.

Tom was dismissed at four o'clock and allowed into the barracks again. He went up the stairs and changed from fatigues to his least rumpled khakis. He walked with a dozen others to the PX which had beckoned almost from the moment of his arrival the evening before. Within 15 minutes they sat at formica topped tables drinking beer or carbonated soft drinks, eating hamburgers and listening to <u>Korea, Korea, Here</u> <u>I</u> <u>come</u>, repeating over and over on the juke box.

Tom had a beer, and then a Coke, and then a pint carton of milk with some vanilla wafers. Sitting there in his starched khakis with his service cap tucked in his belt and watching the other soldiers and the smartness of their uniforms, he began to feel pretty good.

Tom made it back to the mess hall in time for chow which, so far, had been disappointing and was served boiled chicken and mashed potatoes. The cooks and KPs were sweating freely. The back of Tom's shirt was soaked through as well. He was glad to escape the damp heat of the mess hall after the few minutes it took to eat. There were all kinds of clothing and equipment to turn in and to be reissued. Much of the National Guard gear was of pre- and early- World War II vintage. An example is the field pack. Putting one of these in order required rolling the blanket and shelter half into a cylinder and strapping it vertically onto the pack. The canvas harness and webbing were mustard yellow. This pack was replaced with a dark green two-piece pack that had a detachable cargo pack that belted onto the bottom. Tom turned in old shiny woolen pants and shirts and received new issue. He got a new shelter half replacing the old issue that left one end of the tent open, entrenching tool, and gas mask. He got new socks, underwear, field pants, caps and a jacket. The new issue came at a great rate filling the clothes racks and footlockers. He got new low cut shoes that needed breaking in, and the application of a spit shine. There was no consistency in the issue of foot gear. Some Bandsmen drew combat boots with side buckles, others the lace-up so-called jump boots. Special directives were stressed as to the only acceptable shoe dyes and polishes to be utilized.

The foot lockers were organized. Each soldier was to buy articles which were to remain unused in their unopened wrappers for inspection purposes only. These included a toothbrush, toothpaste, soap, shaving cream, razor and blades laid out precisely in the upper tray. Socks were rolled and placed in a special row as peas in a pod. Transgressions of the inspection rules would result in demerits, and demerits meant restriction for the individual or in some all the occupants of the bay.

On Saturday morning the barracks and the soldiers in their khakis were to receive a very thorough inspection. The Company was immaculate. The corners of the stairs had been cleaned with toothbrushes. The windows had been shined with newspapers. The soldiers had not sat down after putting on their khakis for fear of creasing them. The CO swept through and the inspection was over in five minutes.

After the inspection the men were assembled in the lower bay of the barracks for their first Saturday post-inspection Troop Information and Education lecture, the TI&E, and the initial presentation of a staff sergeant who'd been to a special three-day instructors' school preparing for the present eventuality.

In front of the men was a blackboard to which a world map was affixed. The soldiers were told the smoking lamp was lit, that smoking was permitted.

The instructor opened a booklet containing the week's topic outline and in a halting, somewhat disjointed way made his way through, in 40 minutes, with little comprehension on his part, or the men's part for that matter, a description of the peril facing the Free World, and the tasks to be fulfilled by the informed fighting men of the United States of America.

Upon conclusion of the lecture half the Company received passes off the post good until 2400 hours, midnight, Sunday evening. But as there remained 30 minutes until the men could be excused, they all went outside to police the area.

Policing the area was one activity always available to the sergeants when all other activities had run their reasonable course, and it still wasn't time to release the men to lunch, for example, or to permit them in the barracks. Or if there were still 20 minutes before the trucks were scheduled to arrive and they wanted to keep the men and boys under their immediate control, or if some small detail of men were fearful of being assigned another duty that would extend beyond the present one that would see them finished if they could just extend it to a reasonable quitting time, that all-purpose, never fail activity, assuming it wasn't raining, which in itself was a pretty mitigating circumstance, was butt policing the area.

The men and boys would extend in a single rank facing the area to be policed. The supervisor would set the pace which was determined by the size of the area, the number of policers, and the amount of time that needed to be expended. Usually, though, at a stroll, the pacer NCO would set forth with the rank guiding on him. Each policer had one eye for dressing with the advancing line and one eye for cigarette butts. It was the standard procedure that any smoker was to field strip his own cigarette when he was through with it. The glowing end was to be flicked, snubbed or crushed, the paper tube slit with a fingernail, the tobacco shreds shaken loose and scattered; and the cigarette paper rolled into a tight little pill and discarded. As so it was when the smoking was supervised. At such time as the group was advised the smoking lamp was lit, instructions to field strip the butts would be given and those who discarded the butt entire would be impatiently reminded to retrieve and strip it.

But unsupervised soldiers in the manner of their civilian cousins would simply remove the cigarette from their lips when out of doors and discard the cigarette entire, sometimes crushing it under foot, sometimes flipping it away to smolder unattended. These cigarettes were the object of the butt police sweep.

The individual policer dressed with his rank was expected to maintain pretty much a straight course and was especially not expected to deviate in order to avoid having to pick up a butt and deal with it, or to avoid any other discarded object.

Rarely, but only rarely, there might be a scrap of paper or an empty cigarette pack. Then the policer would have one hand occupied for the remainder of the sweep. And even more rarely, only once or twice in the course of hundreds of sweeps, a cigar butt would fall to the lot of one of the group.

Thus it was, a TI&E lecture ended a bit early, butt police. The trucks made good time back from the firing range for chow 20 minutes early, butt police. The NCO was tired of marching drill, 10 minutes butt police. What to do about cork tips and filters? Such accessories were scorned by the military smoker in 1950, and no Kool smokers in the whole Division as far as Tom knew.

CHAPTER 5

The area now policed, Tom, in the first contingent of Bandsmen on pass arranged to ride into the nearest small town for a look see. He rode in with one of the sergeants who had driven his car down from Oklahoma and kept it parked just outside the gate.

The soldiers who were to remain on the post the weekend washed and ironed clothes, polished brass insignia, wrote letters, went to the post theater, or the PX. Several unfortunates drew KP or guard duty.

The 30 minute ride into town was quite without incident. A narrow state highway, two lanes with a mixture of commercial development, private homes, farm equipment dealers. The grass grew high and rank on either side of the heavily patched roadway. Leesville was a town of 3,000 souls, an agricultural center with a short section of its main street dedicated to the needs of the residents of the Army post.

There was a tattoo parlor, a couple of jewelry-appliance stores offering souvenirs and inexpensive wedding rings, cafes offering hamburgers and fries, and a mixture of beer bars and cocktail lounges. Walking up and down the commercial section, Tom was reminded more than not of the little towns he'd lived in in Oklahoma.

There were a few groups of high school age girls already occupied by the more forward of the soldiers who clowned like high school children and asked the girls their names and what church they went to. There were no hard looking professional women on the streets of the small town that afternoon.

Tom was met by one of his Company who asked where he'd been and told him to come on up the street and try this really great mixed drink at this lounge.

It wasn't a bad place, quite presentable. It wasn't a dive. The bartender and waitress were friendly. About five of the Bandsmen were seated around an oval cocktail table drinking whiskey sours. This activity was something Tom had seen before only in the movies. Oklahoma was a dry state. Saloons and beer bars were frequented in his experience only by rough-looking rural customers at the county end of town.

Tom ordered a whiskey sour and marveled at how the citrus disguised and enhanced the ordeal of whiskey drinking. He tipped the waitress a dime, the first time he had ever tipped, and animatedly participated in the drink testing. A Tom Collins was great. A John Collins was also great. The waitress suggested a Moscow Mule, exotic of exotics in 1930. Ginger beer vodka, and ice in a special copper mug.

This was another of Tom's initiations. He didn't become drunk, his friends didn't become loud, or want to fight, or cause trouble, or want to leave, or to throw up in the restroom. They simply decided after a while they'd had enough. They said goodbye to Leesville and drove back to the post and went to bed.

The rowdies started coming back from town and the

PX beer halls about midnight and there were arguments over the light switches, and curses, and stumbling around in the dark, bathes and running water in the shower room for about three hours off and on until things got settled down.

The next morning Tom slept late, until 10:30 or so. The barracks was bright and hot. There was a mixture of made and unmade bunks. Some neatly dressed soldiers returned from church. Others half-dressed and unshaven fussed with equipment or talked about getting coffee at the PX. There were the usual letter readers and writers at their solitary tasks.

What became apparent in a short time were the Bandsmen who felt their separation from home most keenly. They were almost without exception those who were engaged, who had been engaged, or had become engaged just before their departure, and in a half dozen of the cases, the majority of them, they worked at relieving the pain of separation by writing enormously long letters. Happily, they received megaletters in return. These boys were the mail call freaks, and they received from their fiancees large packet-like envelopes containing many pages of pastel paper most often written on in lavender or green ink. They read these letters during breaks and lying on their bunks, and at noon, and in the evening. Then they, in their turn, would set out their letter writing paraphernalia; boxes of stationery, bottles of ink to refill their pens, booklets of stamps. And, if not reading letters in their free time, they would usually be seated on the footlockers at the ends of the bunks, hunkered over, knees pressed together supporting the stationery box writing desk. And, they wrote, and wrote.

They usually, politely, declined invitations to play Hearts, go to the show, drink beer, take a stroll, but sat hunkered sometimes raising a head to gaze into space when temporarily pausing to collect thoughts or to reminisce, or whatever else went on in the process.

Occasionally, a writer would accept an invitation to go get a Coke on a Saturday afternoon. He would comb his hair, put on a little used go-to-town suit of khakis saved for special occasions, and walking to the PX he'd participate brightly and enthusiastically in the conversation like someone on holiday appreciating the break from some kind of demanding routine. And then later he'd sort of slow down, become quieter, and not contribute as much; or he'd respond more absent-mindedly, and he'd excuse himself to go back to the barracks to reconnect via paper and pen to the person he missed so desperately.

The letter writers, the real letter writers, never eased up the whole time Tom knew them, Louisiana on. And those whom he made some contact with after the Army married those girls shortly after arriving back home.

What could they have said in those hundreds of pages making up the hundreds of letters after more than a year's separation, finally going on almost two year's separation? What did they say during the infrequent long distance phone calls made when they were so expensive and a single call from Louisiana to anywhere was tremendously difficult to accomplish, and it would eat up a week's pay in several minutes of staticky conversation?

The central experience for these Bandsmen was an ever increasing pain of separation that appeared not to lessen or alleviate the whole duration of their absence from home and all other physical distress, or excitement, or interest was secondary to this central addiction.

On that Sunday morning Tom lay in bed and read borrowed magazines until time for the noon meal. The chow line was short and the cooks and KPs relaxed and unhurried. For the first time there were second servings for those who wanted them. Boiled chicken, mashed potatoes, canned corn, Jello, bread, iced tea.

Tom returned to the barracks and spent the afternoon and early evening washing uniforms and webbed gear in the laundry tubs in the latrine scrubbing with a GI brush, using blocks of yellowish brown GI soap to scrub the new look off his recently issued clothing. He wanted his khakis a silvery light tan, his fatigues a whitish green. It took elbow grease.

Dinner was early and consisted of sandwiches and tea to let the kitchen crew off. That evening Tom ironed his clothing on the top of his footlocker and shined his low-cut shoes and his boots, putting layer after layer of spit shines on the toes and heels. He rubbed his brass collar insignia, the crossed rifles and the US on a shine cloth wearing the relief off until the insignia retained the shape only, but no detail.

Soldiers began returning from their passes to the

adjacent towns between 8:00 and 9:00 that evening with a crescendo of arrivals about 11:00 and bursts of commotion and disturbance until two or three AM. There was vomiting and scuffling and on one or two occasions a sergeant in his underwear and steaming angry emerged from a squad room to demand quiet and lights out delivered with some other remarks and curses he felt appropriate.

Tom was shaken awake at 4:00 AM by the Charge of Quarters and told that he was to go on KP in the place of some other Bandsman who would be attending to some other Company business that day. Tom was incredibly drowsy but washing his face and brushing his teeth helped rouse him to a shivering wakefulness and 20 minutes later he was walking to the mess hall.

He reported to the back door and was told he'd be doing pots and pans that day as a reward for being the last to report. Several cooks and permanent KPs were sitting around smoking and drinking coffee. Huge stainless steel pans of bacon were in the ovens already. There were boxes heaped with loaves of bread. Already Tom was alert to the possibility of filching food, but as a pot and pan washer he'd learn he'd have little opportunity to grab a can or box of anything.

To Tom's disappointment he learned that he'd receive little or no benefit from being on the inside of the operation. Rations were short and the food often ran out even serving small to moderate portions, and those at the end of the show line often went without a serving of meat.

One of the permanent KPs showed Tom how to build up a sink of sudsy water and cautioned him that the penalty for leaving a bit of grease on a pot was to have the entire run condemned as unsatisfactory and to have to repeat the entire wash and rinse job for that batch of pots and pans. Tom learned that day that pots and pans was the heaviest, dirtiest, most time consuming KP job of them all. Three times he washed the pots, skillets, pans, bowls, and utensils that were dirtied in boiling, stewing, baking, and frying food for over 300 men and boys. Everything was greasy. It was either melted fat, or encrusted grease that was burned on, or charred and required scrubbing with steel pads.

The cooks did inspect each batch minutely and in that respect Tom's work passed muster. But his clothing became sopping wet, befouled with sweat, grease, and soapy water. His hands turned from red to a curious wrinkled white.

The mess hall required an incredible number of cooking utensils most of which were too large to fit even in the oversize sinks, and they had to be balanced and leaned into to be scrubbed and rinsed.

Tom was tired by lunch time and exhausted by midafternoon when he was able to take his first real break. He sat on a box by the back door and smoked a cigarette and talked to another KP who was garbage cans for the day. The entire mess hall had been swept and mopped and all the tables and benches had been scrubbed a second time. The sinks were wiped dry and shiny. It was pretty in a way, but it was as if most of the grease and garbage had been transferred to accumulate on his own clothing, and he was really tired.

For a third time the Job was repeated that evening and Tom washed the cooking pots after the food was carried to the serving line, and then after the chow line was closed down he washed the serving pans and trays and this and that and one more thing until he was thanked and dismissed at 9:00 that night.

Tom made it back to the barracks and after taking off his boots stood under the shower in his clothing scrubbing each layer to rid it of the grease and mess until he was able to work down to himself. He wrapped a towel around his waist, wrung out the clothes and hung them up to dry and went to sleep before lights out at almost the moment that his head touched the pillow.

New faces began to appear in the Company as men and boys auditioned in the day room for transfer into the Band Company. And others left as they were able to obtain discharges for hardship or dependency reasons.

The amount of housekeeping work lessened as the Company settled into its routine and after a week or two Tom's only responsibility after some minor assignment was to stay out of the barracks, but close to the Company area and not to appear idle. Sometimes Tom strode purposefully from one end of the area to the other. It helped to carry something. A clipboard with a sheaf of papers was ideal.

With the relaxation of the work demands the men had more energy in the evening for drinking and gambling. The scattered beer halls in the auxiliary PXs around the post became more frequented and alliances and rivalries between Companies arose.

On occasion 30 or 40 infantrymen would range out into a neighboring artillery or quartermaster company area and run around the barracks kicking the walls and shouting insults. There was always much dizzy laughter and the assault groups were often occupied as well in dragging and carrying those of their own group who succumbed to drooling stupor and in compassionately holding the heads of those with dry heaves and in taking care of those who reeled and ran and bumped into each other for the fun of it. Most of these soldiers were 16- to 18-year-olds.

After such an evening and after everything quieted down at Camp Polk, General MacArthur on the bridge of the Mount McKinley watched the LCVPs carry the Marines to the seawall at Inchon.

The somewhat older group of gamblers got down to business often in a sergeants' squad room but sometimes out in an open bay and, after lights out, in a latrine. A blanket would be draped over a footlocker extending out onto the floor and they would shot craps. There wasn't much cash until the first payday, so they played for markers, scraps of paper with scribbled IOUs, and when that first payday came and the men and boys filed past the pay table in their Class A uniforms they paid off laundry debts, and then just outside the barracks they settled the various gambling debts. Hastily scribbled on scraps of paper were translated into crisp 10 and 20 dollar bills.

This initial experience of paying off decided most of the first-time gamblers against paying further to learn the gambling lessons that must be learned. But for a few it was already too late. They'd learned in a few disastrous hours. One sergeant lost so much money that he was dependent on friends for beer and cigarette money for many months afterwards. He was a real charity case whose needs were met by alms. The sergeant's creditor in this case was a successful crap shooter and poker player, aged 17, who bought a small taxi company in his hometown with his winnings some two years later when he was discharged.

Tom lost $18 in one of the first crap games, and it had taken his breath away at how fast almost three days' wages had gone. He hadn't liked the dynamics of the game either and had no desire to get back for further chances at revenge, or triumph, or whatever it was that motivated the real crap shooters, winners and losers.

There was a lot of drinking in the barracks as the soldiers indulged in the novelty for Oklahomans and teen-agers of buying liquor in package stores. They bought gin, apricot brandy, bourbon, tequila, vodka, cognac, and drank them all warm and straight from the bottle. Among some of the younger soldiers there arose competitions in speed, or the amount of ingestion, dares, bets, and so on, but the consequences of alcohol poisoning were quickly learned by a 17-year-old who offered to chug-a-lug a pint of gin on a $5 bet. He drank the gin without pausing for breath and collapsed after a bit of slurred speech. Someone shoved fingers down his throat, and he vomited across the arm of the first aid administrator and across one bunk as well. He choked apparently inhaling some of the vomit, and his lapse into absolute stupor frightened the onlookers into calling the post medics who carried him out of the barracks on a stretcher never to return to the Band Company. He spent some time in the post hospital and was transferred into some other outfit for disciplinary reasons.

CHAPTER 6

At last the Company began to function as a band playing for reviews and retreats, brief evening ceremonies, riding in open trucks to the different battalion and regimental parade areas and parading and playing as undulating rectangles of men and boys paraded in turn past the reviewing stands.

The Band Company was divided into two smaller bands sometimes to play for two different regiments on the same evening. A dance band was formed for dances at the officer's clubs and small combos were organized to play at NCO clubs, or as entertainment units in the field.

Tom's musicianship was not developed enough for him to function well in the dance band, or in the combos that improvised. The incoming draftees, many of them professional musicians, took most of these responsibilities.

He did play in the dance band on a couple of occasions and played what he could sight reading from the charts. The assistant CO offered him Benzedrine as a simple courtesy, but Tom declined. The older musicians were more interested in drugs than the younger band members who were still fascinated by the violent assaults of alcohol on their behavior and bodies.

Once after an intermission, Tom returned to the bandstand and could get absolutely no sound from his saxophone. He puffed and blew and finally sat and pretended to play. He was humiliated later to find a liquor glass jammed up the bell of the horn, and he wondered if he had been intentionally silenced, or if it had been done merely for a joke.

Tom's one trip off the post had been sufficient to discover he had no interest in returning to Leesville, but one weekend there was an extra seat in an auto going to Shreveport, and he decided to go.

In Shreveport they immediately located the slummy part of town and went looking for liquor and prostitutes. They bought pint bottles of liquor and bottles of Coke and returned to the car and drank and then split up by twos to canvas the cheap hotels.

Tom and a friend entered one and the desk clerk said it was a little early, but if they'd come back around 9:00 that evening he would have some young, clean white girls. Tom's companion went into greater detail with the room clerk. He wanted to know their ages and hair color, and if they were fat. He discussed price, especially for the room, and that was something of a sticking point.

Tom felt a sense of unreality that this could actually be happening and involving him as well, because he knew what they were doing was illegal and immoral and perhaps even physically threatening. He might be robbed, or beat up, or catch a disease, but he was just drunk enough and more greedy to try the experience than fearful of the consequences. He was jittery though and his whole chest felt tight and his breath came shallowly and irregularly.

At 9:00 Tom returned and paid the clerk $5 for an

hour's use of the room and went up the stairs through a dim corridor and found the room apparently clean. It had linoleum flooring and was furnished with an iron bedstead, a dresser with a mirror, and a straight wooden chair. He sat in the chair and waited.

Ten or 15 minutes later the door opened and a girl about 18 dressed in a bathrobe, carrying a basin of water in one hand and a towel over her arm came into the room. She said a straight lay was $10, and then listed several rather more expensive combinations and options. She was brisk and matter of fact, as if she were rather busy.

Tom selected one option that raised the price to $15, which he paid in advance, and the girl told him to remove his boots and pants only, while she got ready, a process that involved nothing but setting the basin on the seat of the chair and laying her bathrobe on the chair back.

She wore only a bra, and Tom saw that one side of her body from the shoulder to the hip had terrible scar tissue from a burn or a scald.

Tom lay on his back and then rolled over on top of the girl after she did what she had been paid the extra $5 to do, and she had done it so well and thoroughly that when the job was completed in the missionary position he felt it was $15 well spent.

She let him relax on top of her for just a moment and then rolled out from underneath him and went to the basin where she squatted to wash and dry herself.

Tom asked her how much she would charge to stay

all night, but she declined saying she never did that. He told her that it was his first time with a prostitute, and she said she didn't believe it and left.

He dressed and went down to the empty lobby feeling that something very good had happened to him. He was sober, rather keyed up by the significance to him of the experience, and he was hungry. Tom noticed that it wasn't quite 9:40.

The Division and the Band Company were about to full strength by now. The Oklahomans had been joined by draftees and a few enlistees from north-central and northeastern states. Many of the draftees were in their middle twenties. They had been drafted late in World War II, had been discharged with less than six months' service, and not being 26 yet were still liable for further service. Most were established in jobs, many were college graduates, few were pleased or even willing to tolerate what was happening to them as a consequence of the geopolitical convulsions taking place only 10,000 miles from their very own shores. Their Polish and Italian names and food packages were exotic to the Oklahomans. From Chicago came aromatic packages of Polish sausage, from New York carefully packed jars of gefilte fish.

The Company didn't split into factions based on regional backgrounds. Real friendships developed between unlikely combinations. A Wisconsin Swede, a Boston Italian, an Oklahoma Scotch-Irish. One of the most exotic newcomers was a stand-up comic and singer who was added to supplement the dance band and entertainment units, who became the particular pet of the Division Commander, a two-star cotton broker from southwestern Oklahoma. This draftee spent most of his time at the officers' club as court jester and was accorded the singular privilege of sleeping late in the barracks, skipping morning formation, to compensate for the late hours of his schedule.

The basic military training of the Company resumed with more field work. The Company would fall-in with field gear and weapons after breakfast and march to a training area for lectures and training experiences. The Bandsmen were issued new gas masks and learned how to put them on quickly. They were crowded into wooden sheds where tear gas was released, and they put on their masks. Some of the less skillful were punished with choking, crying, and some few, vomiting into their masks.

The Bandsmen listened apprehensively as they sat on their steel helmet stools and then one at a time accompanied an instructor into a small bunker where they pulled the pin on a fragmentation grenade and threw it over the wall of the bunker into the grenade range while the rest of the Company, those awaiting their turns, commented quietly on what was happening to them.

They spent hours in firing circles practicing the various firing positions of the rifle working on obtaining sight pictures to match those of the training posters, the tip of the barrel sight held steady against the bottom of the image of the target's bulls-eye, and they squeezed the triggers trying not to jerk or flinch. Then at the live ammunition ranges they fired for the record with their rifles and fired for familiarization only light machine guns, machine pistols, and .45s.

Now that the Band was up to authorized strength, the members went through two-and-a-half-days of aptitude and intelligence testing and personnel reviews. God only knows what the Army hoped to learn and do with the information.

The men and boys dressed in khakis marched across the post to a gymnasium-like hall and took a series of multiple choice tests, each closely timed, their choices of answers made by marking between dotted parallel lines with a special soft-leaded pencil. Each test had its ritual. Fill in the information required for identification. Listen to the instructions read aloud and which were identical for each section. And then the test itself: Book is to paper as brick is to; A. wood, B. cement, C. clay, D. None of these. And then there were geometrical shapes printed from various perspectives. Tom did not mind guessing at all. He enjoyed answering the questions he knew and guessed with no anxiety at the ones he didn't. There were frequent breaks and they stood around smoking and chatting about the questions they remembered.

By this time the UN forces were well landed behind the North Korean lines at Inchon and the parallel drives up the peninsula under way.

The last element was an interview, one to one, about Tom's premilitary employment and special talents. He described his after school jobs at a print shop as a clean-up boy, and at a library as a stack boy and book mender. The interviewer flipped the pages of a book of occupational classifications back and forth and after being persuaded by Tom that he couldn't really, in good conscience, be included in the brotherhood of printers, was declared to a bookbinder in civilian life. That was it. They were all through.

Some weeks later Tom learned the Company had received a list of the names of the Bandsmen who had achieved scores above the cut-off level to permit them to make application for officer training, something around 110 on the IQ test, and that his test was in the 110 to 112 range. Tom was mildly interested that his score was so ordinary. He'd had few intimations that his intelligence was extraordinary, but as he'd never learned the results of any of the scores of achievement and IQ tests taken as a public school pupil, these scores did not leave the question of his basic aptitudes as open-ended as before.

None of the Bandsmen made application for officer training, but a month later two did volunteer and were accepted for the Ranger Company being organized.

The Band continued its basic infantry training, working through squad, platoon, and company level problems, and Tom felt thoroughly at ease walking down the side of a sandy road early in the morning with tank companies churning down the road and trucks with howitzers trailing behind moving to emplacements camouflaged with netting and brush and at the end of the day returning to the barracks to shower and amuse himself.

Some mornings in the barracks there were training movies and lectures. The simulations on the screen involved US troops against an enemy termed the Aggressors whose helmet lines were modified with a vaguely eastern European crest, and who wore exotic insignia and unit identification badges on their GI fatigues.

There were films contrasting the visibility of troops who didn't silhouette themselves against the skyline with those who did, on digging slit trenches in anticipation of a tank attack, one sickening film on gangrene that featured slipping hardened blackened flesh off a great toe bone, and the chaplain came by to show and discuss a couple of films that dealt with the problems and consequences of venereal disease.

The last two films really spoke to Tom and the possibility of syphilis spirochetes lying dormant in his system for 20 years, still dangerous, gave him some very anxious moments and the potential for some future restraint. The venereal disease rate in Louisiana around Camp Polk was breathtaking although it had been, as yet, relatively light with the Oklahoma guardsmen. And they hadn't even been issued prophylactic kits as yet. Some of the more experienced soldiers did use rubbers. The film on the pro kits had been slightly sobering as well with its emphasis on the importance of post coital urination, and then breaking off the metal tip of a small tube of jelly, and then inserting it into the tip of the penis, and forcing the jelly well up into the urethra. It seemed no end of trouble, inconvenient, a procedure of amusement, or insult, or sarcasm to the sex partner, and uncomfortable. The Bandsmen had been examined as a group on Saturday mornings several times specifically for gonorrheal infections. The penalty for concealing the illness was substantial. As far as Tom knew no one in the Band Company had contacted VD.

The road marches extended in duration and distance and the Company at this point in the training was often driven to exhaustion. At the same time the recovery from physical exhaustion became remarkably rapid. The soldiers might be marched out with packs at 6:00 in the morning, making it back at 8:00 or 9:00 that night, but after a few minutes rest and quick shower many could still race to the PX for an hour of prodigious beer drinking and rough horseplay.

One silly mock combat game involved getting quite drunk and then racing on hands and knees through the corrugated metal drain pipes under the company areas, popping out where the pipes opened into ditches, stealing light bulbs from unattended company day rooms, and then tossing the bulbs down the echoing drains like hand grenades and charging back into the pitch darkness.

CHAPTER 7

The governor of Oklahoma is coming to visit his now federalized National Guard division. This visit involves special preparations for the Band company. It learned ruffles and flourishes, a kind of primitive fanfare, a musical cannon salute. Protocol and rank determine how many repetitions of the pattern are to be played on a specific occasion.

The governor is to be greeted at Division Headquarters, and then he will review representatives of one of the infantry regiments much honored by being chosen.

One bright late fall morning the Bandsmen, each burnished and starched, rode in open trucks to the Division Headquarters area. They and the other troops present were inspected and reinspected. Dust was flicked from their spit-shined boots and khaki trousers were neatly bloused over snow-white canvas leggings. They were permitted to smoke with the usual admonition to shred the tobacco remaining in the butts and to roll the paper into tiny pills.

To pass the time the troops were rehearsed, and the inspections were run through again and again. The Bandsmen were ordered to attention and the music played partly and then all the way through.

The troops were thoroughly tired of waiting, and the officers were beginning to have difficulty with horse play breaking out here and there in the ranks when word came down the governor's car was five minutes away. Immediately all was business again. The ranks and files were aligned for the twentieth time and the troops put at parade rest.

A brown sedan nosed around the corner of a building and all the units were snapped to attention. The sedan stopped, an officer emerged from the front seat to open a rear door, a civilian in a snap brim hat got out of the car and all musical hell broke loose.

The governor looked on benignly as he was ruffled and flourished. The Commanding General led him up and down several ranks of troops as the Band played pianissimo in the background. The governor was led to the flagpole where his snap brim hat was held over his heart and the military saluted with hand or weapon and the band rattled out the Star Spangled Banner.

The governor, a slight man in a pearl grey double-breasted suit, got back into the brown sedan and was driven away as the Band played the theme from the musical Oklahoma.

The trucks returned for the Bandsmen who smoked and tipped their white helmet liners back off their foreheads and the infantry detailed to welcome the governor was marched away. The Bandsmen were given the rest of the morning to lie on their bunks or to fool around the Company area.

Reports of the whorehouses in Opelousas worked on Tom's curiosity enough to stimulate his next excursion off the post. But for the prostitutes he was completely happy to spend his leisure immersed in the military routine of the post.

An auto load of Bandsmen arrived in Opelousas about dusk one Saturday and drove up the driveway of an enormous white frame home of some three stories set well back from the street in a neighborhood of spacious yards, large homes, and tall shade trees. In back of the house was a moderate sized parking lot lined off in white diagonal lines into parking spaces.

The Bandsmen walked up the back steps to a screened in porch that extended the length of one side of the house. The porch was furnished with sofas, coffee tables, floor lamps, juke box, and several girls who'd finished an early dinner and were sitting chatting.

The atmosphere here was relaxed and unhurried. A black maid took orders for drinks and the soldiers and the girls got acquainted. One girl moved to sit in a boy's lap, another gestured toward a door, but the soldiers wanted to unwind from the long drive with a beer or two. And the real object of their trip, and curiosity, and visit was still at dinner. Tom had heard about her from a boy in the Quartermaster Company. She was a woman with enormous breasts.

When she did appear, Tom was astonished. Those breasts were big. She was a slight bodied woman, a brunette in her thirties, bright red lipstick. Her whole front was bosom from her neck to her waist.

Tom resolved to pay to see that, but he wasn't fast enough, and four others made quick arrangements to precede him. The other prostitutes became annoyed with Tom and the others who declined their offers of immediate service. Even the madam chided the boys gently for their fixation. She urged them to try at least the other girls, but the Bandsmen resolved to wait their turns at the enormous breasts.

Tom was startled to see two policemen walk onto the porch. He sat stunned with panic as the policemen went up to the madam, said, "Good evening, Ma'm," and inquired politely into the state of her health and solicited her opinion of the weather, if it didn't seem a little cooler than yesterday, and declined her offer of a beer, but said they'd check in again in the course of the evening.

Tom was totally unable to reconcile the sight of the two policemen as unconcernedly polite in a whorehouse as if they'd stopped by a pharmacy or cleaning shop and made a professional courtesy call.

At intervals of 15 to 20 minutes the soldiers emerged from their rendezvous with the prostitute with the huge breasts and finally the madam nodded that it was Tom's turn. He walked into the bedroom and the woman was squatting over a basin washing herself. She asked for his $10 and told him not to remove any clothing but just to pull his pants down. She slipped the robe off her shoulders and her breasts hung down past her waist with enormous areolas the diameter of coffee cups.

It was rather awkward getting onto the bed with his shorts and trousers at his knees. Tom loosened his tie and the woman pushed his shirt tail out of the way. She began a rapid twisting and grinding of her hips, heavy breathing, light moaning, interjections of, "Baby, oh Baby." Tom came in a few minutes but continued pumping until the woman realized he had come, and she rolled quickly out from under him and began washing in a fresh basin of water. She handed Tom a towel to dry himself with and checked the pad on the bedspread to see if it were soiled and needed replacing. She had the robe over her shoulders again as he left the room.

Tom was going to have another beer and tell his buddies how great it had been. It was the first pair of unclothed enormous breasts he'd ever seen. Now whenever he saw a woman with big breasts who was clothed it would be no mystery or big deal, because he'd already seen what enormous breasts looked like.

CHAPTER 8

The Band was detailed to march and play in a number of small town parades in that corner of Louisiana and adjacent Texas. Once they were driven in trucks to Beaumont, Texas, where they performed and then were allowed several hours of free time before the trip back to the post.

Walking past a theater Tom and a friend were asked by an older man in a VFW cap if they'd like free tickets to the theater. They were directed to seats high in the balcony. The performance was under way and after some confusion they ascertained it was a country western jamboree.

They rather scorned the country western dress of the entertainers and were not at all interested until, with an enormous fanfare Tennessee Ernie Ford was introduced and appeared in a snowy white costume trimmed with silver. Tom was amazed by his wit and charm, musicianship and showmanship, and he realized that Ford was the first entertainer worthy of that description that he'd ever seen perform. And while not converted to the corn and sentimentalism of country music, Tom did feel he'd seen a professional.

On the ride back the mini convoy of four trucks drove straight through to make up for the time spent in Beaumont, some of which was really travel time. The pleas to stop for a relief break were rejected and the more uncomfortable and desperate of the Bandsmen tried kneeling at the tailgate to urinate out the back while the trucks maintained their steady 40 miles per hour. The deflection of the wind up and back into the truck caused the desperate ones to wet themselves. There was laughter and anger from the other passengers who pressed forward up against the cab to avoid the spray. Tom, driven by the need close to pain, eventually had to try his luck and sprayed the tailgate and himself as well.

The circus came to Camp Polk. In Korea the NKPA surrendered Pyongyang, the North Korean capital, and an intelligence summary concluded that organized resistance on the part of the NKPA on any large scale had ceased to be an enemy capability.

A dozen Bandsman were detailed to report to the post field house with their instruments, music stands, folding chairs, and the Assistant CO., Warrant Officer Scott.

At the field house there was lots of coming and going. Complicated ropes and wires, slings and platforms were rigged all around the arena.

At one side the Bandsmen set up and folders with the sheets of music that were to be used to introduce, accompany, and dismiss the circus acts were handed out.

The key personnel in this venture were the band director and the drummer who had to follow the performers rather than lead them. This act was typical. A huge dray horse is led to a bank of chimes where the trainer shoves and tugs and the indifferent animal responds by shaking or butting some mechanism that causes the chimes to be struck in some unmetrical approximation of the chorus of The

Bells of St. Mary's. The band director fixes his eyes on the horse's movements and attempts to direct some orchestral accompaniment to the sweaty awkward struggle taking place between trainer, horse, and chime mechanism.

After the mercifully short rendition the lyrical final chord is played by the Band followed by the circus gallop, a quick diminuendo, the frantic shuffling of sheet music and music clips, the fanfares and music to accompany the next act either high-wire artists or clowns, or dogs.

Tom thought all this was great fun. At times he was unable to locate the appropriate music and the tempos really challenged his technique, but the drummer, the lead trumpet, and the clarinet players were totally competent and the Band did a good job.

Initially the circus band members were told they'd receive $6.00 a performance from the circus and Tom's spirits rose each performance as he thought of the accruing multiples of $6.00. There were shows, matinees and evenings, for three days, Friday through Sunday, and by the last performance Tom, himself, felt quite competent as well; something of a veteran circus performer. By this time he had opinions as to the skill and interest of the different acts and decided he would especially miss two young women with good figures who performed on the high wire and whose bandaged ankles and wrists and bruised limbs added the element of poignancy to their thrilling and sensuous performances.

Several days back in the usual routine Tom wondered

why they hadn't as yet been paid their circus stipends and then learned the CO had decided that rather than let the individuals only benefit from the assignment, that the money would be used for the benefit of the whole Company and the folks back home in Oklahoma as well.

A wire recorder was to be purchased with the money and wire recordings of the Band in concert sent back to WKY in Oklahoma City to accompany the regular weekly radio program which reported on the Division's activities and broadcast human interest profiles of the Guardsmen in Louisiana.

This wire recorder, a relatively expensive machine in 1950, will figure in the story again when the Division is preparing to embark from Japan to Korea.

CHAPTER 9

Tom had received but one letter from his mother since leaving Oklahoma two months earlier. He had written twice himself. She had written to thank him for money he sent to her after his first payday. She had said that her contract to teach had not been renewed because of the many absences due to her illness. She said she wasn't sure what she could do, but that adults have problems to solve from time to time and that she would have to deal with hers.

One evening Tom was lying in his bunk in the nearly deserted barracks reading a magazine when a Bandsman appeared at the stairs and told him a Red Cross representative was looking for him. Tom walked down the stairs and was greeted by a middle-aged man who asked him to sit down on the barracks steps with him to talk over some bad news he'd have to tell him.

Tom asked, "Did my mother kill herself?"

The representative said, "Yes, she did."

Tom asked, "Is my little brother all right? And he was told that he was, and that he was staying with his grandmother in Oklahoma City.

When Tom asked how she had died, he was told that she had hanged herself.

The Red Cross representative asked if Tom needed money to go back for the funeral and he said, "Yes." The Red Cross representative said he'd arrange a loan of $45 which should be sufficient to get to Oklahoma City and back, and that he would contact Tom's company commander in the morning to arrange for an emergency leave.

A few minutes after Tom thanked the representative for his offer of any further assistance if needed, Tom walked back up the stairs to his bunk where he lay down and held the magazine.

The next morning Tom was called out of formation to the orderly room. The CO told him that he was granted an emergency leave of three days, four if he needed it, and that one of the sergeants who owned a car would also be given leave to drive him back to Oklahoma City where his grandmother lived and where the funeral and burial would take place.

Tom put some clothing in a duffel bag, then he and the sergeant drove to the Red Cross office where Tom signed a promissory note and received, in turn, the $45.

Tom felt strangely at peace while being driven back to Oklahoma. He watched the road with the driver. He read the billboards to himself. He observed the road surface change from patched concrete to asphalt. The weather was sunny but cool. They stopped at a roadside diner at the edge of a small Oklahoma town, and Tom ate a hamburger and fries, potato salad, and a vanilla milkshake. He smoked many cigarettes.

That night Tom was dropped off at his grandmother's home. He greeted her and his little brother. They talked a little about the funeral arrangements.

His little brother had come home from school. He looked for his mother and found her body mostly concealed by the clothing, dresses and coats hanging by her neck from a cord coming down through the crawl space into the attic. Tom was told some more details of the suicide and its discovery that he didn't want to hear.

My brother will tell you about the death of our mother: "I wasn't told why Mother put me in Putman City School, but I liked it very much. I made lots of friends. I got to take the trombone. It was a long ride on the bus. I caught the bus at the grocery store. The bus went west and south, and then east around the outskirts of Bethany.

"When I came home, I would practice my trombone, or play at a neighbor's house, or go across town to Buddy Legg's. One afternoon Buddy and I came to the house after school. I told him to wait outside while I checked in with Mother. Our mother was up, which was unusual. She seemed agitated and was moving around the house from room to room. I looked down the hallway and saw a noose hanging from the hole in the attic. I grabbed a chair from the bedroom and stepped on it to reach the rope. I was surprised it took my weight. I said nothing to her about it. I just told her I was going to Buddy's for a while and left.

"When I returned an hour later, Grandmother's car was there. Inside the house a heated exchange was going on. The rope had been taken down. Grandmother was angrily telling Mother she'd have to stop this or she was going to be sent back to Norman. Our Mother was wailing, 'No, no,' and saying she wouldn't go.

"She died several days later on October 30, 1950. I remember that morning, before I went to school I laid my Halloween costume neatly across the bed. Mother came to the door when I left for school. She said, 'Good-bye,' and I said, "Bye'. I walked 20 feet across the yard and she said, 'Bob?', and I called back, 'What?' She said, 'Good-bye,' and I laughed and repeated with emphasis, 'Good-bye!'

"I decided that day to walk home from school. It was quite a long walk, longer even than I was used to going on my bicycle. I meandered through downtown Bethany, past Bethany High School. I saw Charlotte McLain and a black-haired girl who gushed big 'Hi's', looked at my trombone case and giggled how cute I was. When I arrived home, I was surprised and pleased that Mother was not about. Perhaps she'd finally gone to work. I went in my room. I was there for quite some time before I became uneasy. It was not likely she'd be so late.

"I went into her room calling her loudly. I threw back the covers, looked under the bed, went to the closet and there I saw her slumped back in behind the clothing. I couldn't see above her waist. She wore her grey housecoat.

"I ran into the street. I suppressed the urge to scream. I knew Mrs. Jones would still be at work. I ran to the Campbell's across the street. She ran back to our house with me. She grabbed Mother's wrist and said, 'She's dead.'

"I pleaded, 'Are you sure?' repeatedly, and she was

emphatic. We stood for a long while holding each other and crying. I was sobbing, 'What's going to happen to me?'

"She took me to someone's house to get me out of sight of the ambulance. Mrs. Campbell was a nurse which may explain why she did everything so correctly. I remember nothing else that day except I stayed at the Jone's that night.

"The next evening the Jone's daughter was going trick or treating. I wanted to go too. I went to the house, opened the door, got as far as the bedroom and flicked on the light. I ran terror-stricken from the house. I told them I had changed my mind. I was embarrassed to ask someone to go get the costume.

"I had asked someone how Mother died, and I was told it was a heart attack. I began to hear other stories in the neighborhood so someone decided I should be told the truth. Maxine grabbed my arm sharply and ushered me into the bathroom and closed the door. She blurted out, 'Your mother committed suicide.' I cried a long time expressing my shame and disappointment she'd not died a natural death.

"When we went shopping for a blouse, I asked why it had to have a high collar. I was told it looked better. I never knew the exact cause of her death until I looked at a photostat of her death certificate in 1958."

They had sandwiches, and soup and iced tea for a late supper and Tom and his brother went to bed.

The next morning after breakfast Tom's grandmother drove him and his brother downtown in her '46 Ford to shop for a high-necked blouse that would conceal the rope marks on his mother's neck. They went to several stores and Tom remained indifferent to the selections and declined to state a preference when a decision was to be made finally between two similar high-necked blouses.

They lunched at a basement cafeteria and Tom's grandmother showed him the newspaper clipping reporting his mother's death which omitted any reference to suicide but stated merely that she died at home, she was the widow of Harold Sterns MacLean, that she was survived by two sons; Bobby, 10, and Thomas, who was serving with the 45th Division at Camp Polk, Louisiana; her mother, Nellie P. Miller of Oklahoma City and two sisters, Mrs. Robert Bobo and Miss Helen Miller and that funeral plans would be announced.

After lunch they drove to the funeral home so that the boys could see their mother. Tom objected and felt the same reluctance and fear he had felt five years earlier when he had been firmly led to his father's coffin and had glanced unwillingly at his father's face and had witnessed his grandmother shrieking and touching his father's body.

They went in the funeral home and his grandmother gave the attendant the blouse and answered some questions about their wishes, and then they went into a viewing room and Tom glanced at his mother's face in the casket and then turned away, and in response to several questions assured his grandmother that that was fine and he was ready to leave; and no, he didn't want to spend any more time looking into the coffin and he said, yes, to every comment made by his grandmother about how peaceful his mother looked. He felt very badly but kept moving toward the door.

His mother's half-sister, married to an engineer in Pennsylvania, appeared before they left and Tom said, "Hello."

She told his grandmother that the grey cloth-covered coffin was cheap looking and criticized its appearance so effectively that an agreement was reached to provide Mariana with a more appropriate coffin for next day's service and burial.

Fortunately, Tom was not involved in the casket decision. It mercifully consisted merely of the imposition of the daughter's will upon her mother's, and at its conclusion Tom said he'd like to remain downtown a while and would catch a bus back home.

His aunt, his grandmother, and his brother left, and Tom walked several blocks to a movie theater. He went to one movie and when it was over, he walked across the street and sat through another.

He caught a bus to his grandmother's neighborhood and had a sandwich at a drug store for dinner. At his grandmother's he pressed his khaki uniform for the next day and polished the brass collar insignia with a Blitz cloth, shined his shoes and went to bed.

The next morning was cool and overcast. After breakfast Tom sat in the living room until it was time to drive to the funeral home. Tom was taken to a small side room where he sat with his brother, grandmother, and some other family members.

Tom sat quietly and did not listen to the stranger who spoke, possibly the minister of some church or other his mother may have attended.

There were flowers, a lot of them, big sprays of gladiolas. When the family was directed to view the coffin, Tom noticed slightly surprised that the auditorium-sized room was quite full, and he recognized family friends from communities far from Oklahoma City, even parents of classmates of his who had not known his mother.

They went somewhere else in the building and sat for some time, and then they went through a side door to ride in the funeral limousine to the burial site.

The auto was enormous and plush, and smelled of grief. His little brother sat on a jump seat. It was raining. His face and body felt heavy and awkward. There were many events happening over which he had no control, and he felt no interest in them. He felt nothing but this heaviness. He listened to his breathing.

They drove into the graveyard. The cars that had preceded them were parked along the curving asphalt drive. They walked to an awning over the grave, a green felt-covered mound of earth, the flowers were there, the coffin was supported over the grave. Many people now offered hands and condolences and expressed their wishes to help in any way.

Tom sat on a folding chair for a while and then left and was relieved it was over. His thought had been, when he had thought, that now both parents were dead and that his mother's death was inevitable given the history of her illness and that was that.

Back at Camp Polk he accepted the condolences of those who knew of the event, and he resumed the tasks that were assigned to him.

Volunteers, 100,000 Chinese volunteers are in Korea now. The ROK II Corps is decimated. Elements of the 1st Cav cease to exist in the fighting around Unsan. U.S. air strikes cause awesome Chinese carnage.

Several weeks later Tom received a strange little letter from one of the starched housedress clad girls from high school. She wrote that an acquaintance of his in the Band had written home how unaffected and cold Tom had been after learning of the death of his mother, especially when he had resumed the magazine reading. The girl wrote that she didn't think it fair that such stories should be told about him.

Tom responded briefly in a note that he had experienced sadness and a sense of loss, and that was about it. He hoped she was enjoying school, and that Army life wasn't bad so far except for the food.

After Tom sealed the letter and addressed the envelope he sat and reflected just a bit. There was nothing that could have happened that would have improved the chances of things turning out any better for his mother. He was only grateful to circumstances that his little brother had not been physically injured in the final unhappy days.

CHAPTER 10

Although Tom was uninterested there were some soldiers who linked up with the civilians of the neighboring communities. The usual initial contact was through attendance at Sunday school and other church sponsored activities for young people. And there were occasionally young girls who would respond to the boys who approached them on the street, or in the soda fountains, or at the skating rink. But the primary social life in the small west central Louisiana farm center was the church, Sunday school, church services, prayer meetings, ice cream socials, covered dish dinners and revivals.

One Bandsman who had a car asked Tom if he'd like to double date to a picture show with one of a pair of girls he had met at church.

Tom was dropped off to introduce himself while the driver went to pick up the other girl and circle back and pick them up. The girl's mother met Tom at the door and said her daughter wasn't quite ready yet, but would he like to come inside and wait. As it was a warm evening Tom said, "Oh, no thanks. I'll just fuck around out here."

That experience became Tom's contribution later when conversations turned to the way fuck and fucking had seized on their language at Camp Polk leech-like or remora-like, and that absolutely no other words came close to stating with such exactness and precision the speaker's most heartfelt feelings about what he was concerned with at the time, the verbal window to the soul: The fucking Army, pass the fucking butter, that fucking corporal, my fucking boots, the fucking chaplain, some fucking beer, my fucking girlfriend, that cheap fuck, fucking cigarettes, fuck off, fuck me, fuck you, fuck them. Those words were visited now and then on unsuspecting family and civilian friends to no little embarrassment to the utterer.

Thanksgiving and Tom's 17th birthday came and went. The U.S. attempted to introduce a resolution in the UN calling for the removal of Chinese troops from Korea. Good try. MacArthur hoped to get the boys home by Christmas. Good try. On November 26, 1950 the Chinese counter-attacked and the 8th Army barely escaped intact.

The Division had by now received its full complement of fillers and for all intents and purposes was at full strength. And the Division for whatever the effect might be on the experience of an individual was training hard in the field. Many exercises now involved live ammunition and so-called culminating kinds of training activities pitting regimental and other large troop movements against aggressor units under the eyes of observers from outside the Division.

It was winter and to Tom's surprise the sunny south was cold. What was described as a cold snap of a week's duration coincided with a breakdown of the system that supplied heat to the barracks and buildings of a large section of Camp Polk. There was a snowstorm, quite an event for this section of the south, then sleet and freezing rain that left a three-inch layer of ice on the ground and vegetation. The temperature was well below freezing when the heat failed.

At first the regular routine was maintained, but as that became impractical most of the affected units were relieved from training tasks and told to just try to keep warm.

The water in the butt cans froze. The ink in the ink bottles froze. The men and boys piled layer upon layer of clothing on and were permitted to lie abed if they wished. It was like a week long weekend with only the basic housekeeping duties assigned.

Tom wore his woolen WWII overcoat with its brass buttons over his field jacket and hood, two pairs of pants, woolen and fatigue. His feet were aching cold most of the time. There was little to do. Regular field training would have resulted in cold related injuries, so the soldiers sat, or lay, on their bunks and heaped abuse upon the fucking cold. After a week the cold released its grip, the heat came back on in the barracks, and the less harsh winter rains of that region resumed. Getting wet and cold was still uncomfortable but with warm barracks to return to it was possible to deal with. They played war to prepare the Division for frisking around the hills and dales of the Korean peninsula. But little did the men and boys suspect this destination who were anticipating rather the barracks of occupied Germany.

As it was, Tom knew little of the political and military events that had resulted in the mobilization and training of his Division. The weekly TI&E lectures were quite removed from any sense of actuality. Some of the soldiers were intensely interested in the progress of the war in Korea, of the possibility of the utilization of Taiwanese troops, of the extent of the intervention of the Red Chinese, and especially the rumors abounding as to the mission of the 45th. Most of the soldiers hoped to remain in the U.S. but others hoped to be stationed in Germany, or elsewhere in Europe. Other rumors proposed the Division for replacement duty in the Canal Zone, or even garrison duty in Hawaii. But almost all were stunned to learn officially shortly before Christmas that the Division was to be sent to Japan.

First of all, the powerful senior Senator from Oklahoma had declared categorically that no Oklahoma National Guard Division of his would be sent outside the continental limits of the U.S., short of a formal declaration of war by Congress.

Second, the Division was a European Theater of Operations Division. Oklahoma units had been part of the Rainbow Division in World War I, and the 45th had fought in North Africa and Europe in World War II just five years before. Many of the officers and senior non-coms were veterans of those campaigns. To be sent to Japan was a novel and unsettling experience.

One weekend Tom was persuaded to leave the post and accompany a Bandsman to Lake Charles where some service organization had arranged for townspeople to open their homes to visiting service men. The family experience and implied wholesomeness of it all, which usually included some church activity, served in some small way to counteract the drunken depravity which was the usual fare of many of the young soldiers and airmen stationed at the nearby military bases.

So, in good time Tom shared a ride to Lake Charles, and he and his companion were met in a very nice residential neighborhood by a very kind woman who greeted them with lemonade and showed them to their bedroom, and gave them towels and invited them to breakfast the next morning. She excused herself and left them alone.

Tom's companion was veteran of these excursions and felt quite at home accepting the hospitality. The boy had developed a wide acquaintance among the young people in the community of the First Baptist Church of Lake Charles. He usually wore civilian clothes on those weekends. He went to ice cream socials, he played basketball, he danced attendance on well-groomed untouchables with names like Linda Sue and Jo Ella.

Tom, on the other hand, felt immensely uncomfortable and out of place. It was like visiting a distant relative. He had no interest in, in fact, a positive horror of the high school give and take of the Baptist Youth Fellowship. Thus, a compromise course of action was worked out. They walked around Lake Charles in uniform. Tom had no civilian clothing, so his companion accommodated him by wearing khakis also.

Tom refused an offer to be introduced at the Teen Center which offered ping pong and soda pop. They ate at a cafe with slot machines ranged along one wall. They attended a double feature. Tom's companion declined an invitation to drink beer at one of the seedy bars at the lower end of the main street. They walked home and slept in a huge soft bed that smelled of body powder and bath salts.

The next morning, they were served breakfast by their hostess. Her husband had some early Sunday morning real estate business errands to run and wasn't there. There was a plenitude of china; cups, saucers, different sized spoons to choose from, very different from the stainless steel and aluminum Tom was accustomed to feeding off of. Their host returned home, and Tom's companion and their hosts went off to church. Tom remained behind to look at the Sunday paper and to read old magazines, and to look through the books in the family library which included a marriage manual.

Their return ride to camp picked them up shortly after the return of the family from church. They stopped off in a cafe for lunch and were back at the post by 4:00 that afternoon.

Two older sergeants, slightly disreputable types in their late 30's, invited Tom once to accompany them to the whorehouses of Port Arthur, Texas. Tom decided he might as well go. He reasoned that after all this is supposedly what he and his buddies were looking forward to last summer when they talked about all the screwing they were going to do once they got in the Army. So, this was it. It was sort of like being in the Louvre and how would you explain not going to see Winged Victory and the Mona Lisa. Here you were up to your ears in whorehouses. You might not get another chance like this later on in life. Let's go rather than look back in sorrow and regret someday.

Those two sergeants were quite a pair. They'd organized crap games, crab feeds, and drinking bouts and now they were promoting whorehouses for the fun of it. Tom sank down in the back seat of their car and listened to their improbable stories and dirty jokes, and they paid little attention to him.

When they got to Port Arthur in the middle of the afternoon, they drove to a shabby district of brick warehouses mostly. They rang a doorbell and identified themselves over an intercom and the door buzzed for them to open it. They climbed dark stairs to another door, a little window in the door opened. Then they were in a long narrow room furnished with stuffed chairs and leatherette covered couches, a juke box, small windows, high, near the ceiling. They joined several lounging soldiers without exchanging greetings.

A door opened at the end of the room and half a dozen girls in costumes similar to those worn by the high-wire performers filed into the room. These were good-looking girls. Net stockings and high heels, the bodices of their costumes pushed their breasts up high.

A girl, a young woman really, came to sit on the arm of Tom's chair and asked him if he liked her. He said he did, and she took him to her room. It was small, one of a number on either side of a long corridor. There was a dressing table with lots of cosmetics, a double bed with a satin spread.

The young woman unzipped the back of her costume and it came off in a piece. Tom noticed the boning inside it that had formed her figure. Tom undressed and lay beside her on top of the spread. She did some things and moved her hips making low moans in her throat and encouraged him and in a few moments he ejaculated.

She handed Tom a towel, cleaned herself and told him their date was $10. He lay the money down by the cosmetic jars and got dressed while she zipped up her costume and combed her hair. She led Tom further down the corridor to a flight of stairs that led to the street where the car was parked, and he stood by the car and waited for the two sergeants.

Their next stop was a really depressing house with linoleum on the floor, a place where two grotesquely obese sisters sold themselves. They all drank beer while the sergeants gossiped with the two women and Tom sat quietly and wondered if the girl in the costume had transmitted some venereal disease to him.

CHAPTER 11

The Bandsmen were told more about their assignment to Japan. The Division was to assume the occupation Army responsibilities on Hokkaido Island. The Division Headquarters was to be at Camp Crawford outside the City of Sapporo. They were taking the place of the 1st Cav which had been thrown at Korea. The 45th was to continue its training in northern Japan for some higher level of combat readiness.

This news gave new impetus to the Division's activities. Soldiers were detailed to two- and three-day schools to learn how to prepare and crate materials for shipment, how to load and unload boxcars. Arrangements were made by the Bandsmen to send accumulated personal belongings and autos back home. More items of equipment were turned in and newer, or more recently designed equipment issued in turn. Questions about leave were unanswered until almost at the last moment in the middle of December the troops learned that half the Division would receive three days' leave at Christmas and the other half three days at New Years, just prior to the Divisions embarcation.

This meant the possibility of a day, or even a day-and-a- half at home for many of the Oklahomans. But few of the soldiers from very much farther away could make arrangements or afford the travel costs to their homes. Tom read from the roster that he was in the half of the Band receiving 72-hour passes at New Year's.

Christmas passed with no particular observance on Tom's part He exchanged no gifts. On the post was an air of urgency and seriousness about whatever they were doing that seemed to affect them all. Christmas, they ate turkey and ate the hard candies and smoked the cigars that were handed out after the meal.

Material that was not to accompany the troops on the voyage to Japan was dispatched to the railhead daily in enormous crates of sweet yellow pine with stenciled identification codes in black all over the outside. The supply room shelves became bare. The post services were minimal. The fever pitch of physicals and inoculations gradually slackened as the men nursing their tender and swollen arms put their shot records in places of safe keeping, mindful of the painful duplication of the shots for anyone unable to produce his initialed record slip.

Some of the Bandsmen whose physical condition, or vision limited them to stateside duty were transferred to other units of the 4th Army to remain at Camp Polk.

One Saturday morning during the TI&E lecture while the soldiers who were going on pass sat in glazed-eye impatience and those not going on pass simply sat glazed-eyed, the CO came in. A Bandsman sitting near the door shouted, "Attention!" All feet slammed against the floor, and so they stood until the CO murmured, "At ease."

Those Bandsmen not going on pass were to fall immediately in formation outside the day room. Half the group filed out of the barracks onto the sandy area with its fingers of Bermuda grass reaching here and there and were told while standing at attention what was required of them.

The Commanding General of the 3rd Division was to pay an informal social call on his old comrade in arms, the Commanding General of the 45th Division. There would be, of course, a small honor guard from the Division Headquarters Defense Platoon, but the Commanding General of the 45th wanted something special also in the way of greeting, a sentimental gesture as it were, for these are sentimental men. He wanted a chorus of GIs singing the old World War II song these two generals had sung back in Italy when the two companion divisions had fought shoulder to shoulder up the Italian boot.

The Bandsmen were to learn the song this morning, sing it in the afternoon, and then they'd be excused. This is the song:

I wouldn't trade my old ODs

For all the Navy's dungarees

'Cause I'm the fighting pride

Of Uncle Sam.

On all the posters that I read

It says:

The Army Builds Men

Well, they're tearing me down

To build me over again.

I'm just a dogface soldier

With a rifle on my shoulder

And I eat a Kraut for breakfast Every day.

So pass the ammunition

To the men of the 45th and 3rd Divisions

Uncle Sam's soldier boys're OK.

The Bandsmen's first reaction to the song involved some sideways glances, but the slight tentative laughs were not encouraged by the stern, no-nonsense approach of the CO. The soldiers were intimidated into singing a straight-forward, if not totally sincere, rendition of the tune.

The visiting general was to arrive on the post in time for lunch, so before noon the soldiers were hustled into a truck and deposited near the Division Headquarters building steps. They were arranged in a platoon-like formation diagonal to the walk up from the street on the newly mown lawn.

The brown sedans and jeeps arrived before there was time for a cigarette break. The generals stepped from a sedan. The Commanding General of the 45th touched the visitor on the arm and nodded to the CO of the Bandsmen. The soldier chorus belted out the song, singing it through twice. The Commanding General of the 3rd smiled, nodded his surprise at the lovely gesture, and lightly punched the

Commanding General of the 45th on the arm before turning to inspect the Defense Platoon.

CHAPTER 12

Some parents of underage Guardmen intervened, and their children were sent back to Oklahoma for discharge and a return to high school. The CO knew Tom was 17 and told him he could transfer to remain in Louisiana if he wished; but Tom told him he wanted to accompany his friends, and the CO responded, "Good enough."

Tom was unable to find a ride, so he and another soldier decided to hitch hike back to Oklahoma City for their 72-hour New Year's pass supposing that they could make better time than a bus as they'd be in uniform, and they were counting on the drivers of west-central Louisiana, northeastern Texas, and south-central Oklahoma to recognize their situation and pick them up.

But hitch hiking was slow and the rides they did get were short. After making 70 or 80 miles between 1:00 PM and dark, they sat, or stood, at the outskirts of a small Texas town until the next morning. A series of rides got them to Oklahoma City late that afternoon. They decided to meet the day after and take a bus back to avoid the possibility of spending another night standing by the side of the road on the return to Camp Polk.

They had been permitted to leave the post a bit early and were not due back until 8:00 AM rather than midnight, so the three days allowed for the pass were almost four. They calculated they had almost 36-hours before they had to catch the bus. Tom went to his grandmother's where after saying hello, he ate some canned soup and crackers and went to bed.

The next morning Tom telephoned one of the girls he'd gone to high school with, and with whom he'd exchanged a few letters. She invited him to her parents' house for New Year's Eve. Tom pressed his uniform, polished his shoes and brass, and late in the afternoon took a city bus to her house.

He had dinner with the family and very self-disciplined avoided any verbal gaffes. Her parents invited them to accompany them to a neighborhood party, but the girl declined saying they would rather listen to records and talk. She and Tom sat on the couch and talked. She asked him many questions about his experiences and told him how he and the other boys were missed from all the Senior class activities, and how the yearbook was going to be dedicated to them. She gossiped about the high school teachers, and the boys and girls still there, and then later quite cosily they petted with much breathing and straining and moist kisses.

They were both quite mussed by that, and before the parents came home, they washed their faces, and straightened their clothing, and combed their hair. But still their lips were swollen, and Tom felt awkward and quite ready to leave when the parents returned. He said that he wasn't hungry and accepted a ride back to his grandmother's and sat quietly and thanked them quietly and reservedly.

The next morning, he telephoned his little brother,

now staying with an aunt and uncle on a farm northwest of Oklahoma City. He said good-bye to him and then good-bye to his grandmother as she drove him to the bus station. Tom's friend wasn't there to catch the bus, so he prepared to spend many hours by himself.

In the bus Tom was invited to join a very noisy group of partiers in the back who somehow impressed him as permanent residents, they were so settled in; but he remained somewhat subdued and never did enter into the communal silliness of the shared liquor and cigarettes of the several girls and sailors. He wasn't attracted by their coarseness and airs of worldly wisdom.

Those girls there in the back weren't more than 16, and they could actually joke about dicks and hard ons, and which sailor had a hard on; and the sailors talked about tits and knockers. All that party had to offer was crudities and gross humor, and after an initial welcome into the bosom of the club, Tom had little to offer in the way of reinforcement of their behavior or novelty, and he drifted from the center of attention.

Tom arrived at the bus station in Leesville in the frosty 2:00 AM darkness, took a cab out to the post and had three hours sleep before reveille.

And now with everyone and everything ready to go, the gear that couldn't be carried in bags, on backs, and under arms, had been crated and sent ahead. The time weighed heavily.

There was only minimal housekeeping now. No passes off the base. Practical jokes became the principal occupation. One Sunday Tom dozed off in the barracks. He was awakened with a, "Jesus Christ! Everybody's in formation! They're looking for you!" Tom looked wildly around the empty barracks, threw on his clothes and dashed down the stairs to the empty Company street. At first confused, and then feeling foolish Tom realized it was still Sunday night and not pre-dawn Monday morning.

Another joke that required a more elaborate ruse to capture its ever more suspicious victims was played mostly on those who acquired reputations of fastidiousness, who were the most disgusted and dismayed when assigned latrine duty. Latrine duty required scrubbing each fixture and surface with GI soap or scouring powder and further required immersion to the elbow in each of the long rank of commodes. A prime success was counted when a tortured commode scrubber could be lured away from a bowl on some pretext to permit the joker to rush to deposit his husbanded after breakfast turd into a freshly scrubbed, but not yet inspected bowl in the few moments the dupe made his reluctant absence on the chance the call away was legitimate.

And on one overcast chill-wintery day the barracks was emptied of everything but metal cots with mattresses folded in half on them, and the Bandsmen stood in the Company street with full field packs, duffel bags, weapons, instrument cases and they were marched at route step to the railhead where they were entrained for New Orleans.

There was water on the train. Each Bandsman carried a full canteen. The smokers had cartons of cigarettes and plenty of matches, and they sat easily and talked quietly as the troop train went through the sandy pine forests and swamps.

Once in New Orleans, they were taken by truck from the train to Camp Leroy Johnson, a post with an air of permanence and civilization to it compared to the primitive slap dash of Camp Polk where all was change. There were wide avenues bordered by palm trees, extensive lawns around low buildings that had screened in verandas and were bordered by large masses of colorful flower beds tended to by civilian gardeners. The dining hall was cool and breezy. The soldiers assigned to the post wore ties with their khakis and strolled unhurriedly in groups of two or three.

The Band's mission was to be transported to the docks of the port of New Orleans whenever elements of the Division boarded troop ships, to play the troops aboard, and then farewell as the ship cast off and went down river to the gulf. The Bandsmen were in their turn to board one of the last of the group of ships required to transport the Division to Japan.

The Band would be bussed or trucked to the dock area and would play marches for the time it took the troops to climb the long gangways up into the ship, for the lines to be cast off, for the transports to be pulled and pushed by tugs into the river channel.

Tom, himself, was eager to board and begin the voyage. He, of course, had never been to sea. He had never seen the ocean.

One afternoon after playing the troops off those Bandsmen who wished to remain in town were excused to amuse themselves and then find their way back to the post on their own. The sightseeing was preceded by a sorting out of who was to accompany whom. Certain of the more sophisticated draftees were asked in a general way if they were going into town. The warmth or specificity of the reply determined the set of the next inquiry and was strictly speaking unnecessary because the answer might be, "I'm going to check things out. Want to come with me?" But occasionally if the reply had hinted of welcome but didn't literally state the invitation, the solicitor might obtain the clarification by the question, "Need any company?" To which the answer would probably be, "Well, I've got some business to take care of." The questions would be dropped at that. Except by one or two of the shameless fans who craved the company of the admired ones. And then it was embarrassing even though occasionally the admired one might wearily suffer the importuner's tagging along. But only to chauffeur or to pay more than his share. There was no guarantee the shameless one might not be abandoned midway through the excursion. He might return from a restroom to find the party departed. All this was made more difficult too, because the sophisticated soldiers with their dry wit and man-about-town imaginations often preferred solo excursions.

This trip into New Orleans, Tom had the company of three or four, too many, of the more puppyish, younger Bandsmen who, while not scorning strong drink were just as interested in hamburgers, milk shakes, and picture shows. It would be less likely for them to initiate or share a low drunken debauch in a really low threatening tavern, or to participate in the minor trashy vandalism that the thought of New Orleans seemed to incubate in Tom's imagination.

Their recreation began with a rather breathless loping tour of the French Quarter, popping in and out of rather wholesome souvenir and candy shops and bars that led Tom to believe the main entertainment was to be found probably off the main drag and more into the neighborhoods. They briskly obtained the lay of the land and accumulated a few paper sacks of souvenirs to Tom's disgust, who traveled light and scorned such obvious artifacts of tourism.

In the middle of the afternoon they happened on one of the admired sophisticated man-of-the-world draftees sitting solo at the counter of an oyster bar, half or more, sozzled on stingers. They crowded round him, and he humorously explained how the oysters on the beds of ice along the wall opposite were eaten and what a stinger was composed of; brandy and white crème de menthe, and they shuddered. Tom ordered a stinger and drank it down and ordered another, and then he ate four oysters before he left with his group that had waited impatiently at the door.

Tom left with them quite dizzy from the effect of the experience. They crossed and recrossed the narrow streets admiring the wrought iron incorporated into the architecture. Their dinner was red beans and rice.

After dark they finally permitted a tout to steer them into a strip joint where they sat at a small round table just in front of the stage. The six ounce bottle of beer was $2.25. The only interesting stripper in the whole bunch did wild things with tassels, but it definitely was not erotic and when the waitress told them it was time to buy another beer they got up and left mid-performance of the stripper, the saxophone player, and drummer, and went outside and walked the side streets looking into windows where families sat eating their suppers. And then it was time to go back to the post.

The Bandsman in their turn were trucked to the warehouse dock in full gear, had numbers chalked on their steel helmets and climbed the long gangplank to a door in the side of the ship. The rails were crowded with soldiers previously boarded, the MSTS in khaki and the cooks in white.

They went in single-file along the inside corridors stepping high and dragging their duffel bags over the water-tight doorways. They struggled down open steel steps trying to maneuver themselves and their gear down four levels to the D deck and their compartment.

Tom's initial impressions were of the vibration of machinery in the all metal environment, the faint yellow light, the odor of oil, the slick oiliness of the grey painted bulkheads and decks, the staleness of the air.

The compartment consisted of a small central open

place surrounded by tiers of metal bunk frames, five bunks high. Canvas laced to the frame made the sleeping surface. The bottom bunk was inches off the deck, the upper bunk well over his head.

They were told to sling their rifles from the bunk frames, their duffel bags would go at the foot of their bunks. They each received two blankets. The band instrument cases would be stored in the bunks during the day and stacked in a corner of the compartment at night. The sleeping quarters were off limits except to the cleaning details during the day.

Tom received his red cardboard meal ticket which he was to present for punching at each of the two meals to be served each day. Breakfast was at 7:00 AM and dinner at 4:00 PM.

There was a lot of palaver about whether to try to feed the Bandsmen that evening. Things were running a bit behind schedule. But, at last, the decision was made to extend the day of the cooks and KPs and the Bandsmen would be fed dinner.

Tom found the chow line and then traced it to its end up stairs and through corridors and up stairs again. The men and boys stood or sat on the stairs while the line moved forward at irregular intervals.

Finally, Tom was at the bulkhead door where an MP in fatigues punched the first of the holes in Tom's meal card allowing him to move into a large low-ceilinged compartment. On his left before the steam table serving line were stacks of metal trays steaming hot water and large metal baskets of knives, forks and spoons. A KP rushed from the galley and hurled more eating gear at the stacks of trays and baskets.

The rest of the compartment across from the serving line was filled with rows of waist high counters affixed to poles where men stood eating their evening meal. There was shouting and clattering. The men were urged to hasten through the chow line. Tom thrust his wet tray at the servers behind the steam table. Two slices of bread, a gob of butter forked from a bowl of water, mashed potatoes, creamed hamburger gravy, green beans, a canned peach half, and coffee.

The deck was slick with spilled food, the air close with the steaming odors of oil and food. Tom found a place at a counter littered with crumbs and spilled food and ate everything on the tray. He shoved the empty tray through a slot to the KPs. While he was eating the troopship had cast off, and when he made his way back up on deck there were groups of men and boys sitting watching the lights on shore, of the other ships, and the stars. Tom was told he could not smoke on deck at night, so he went below and had a cigarette before returning to the deck where he lay on his back on a tarpaulin covered hatch until he wanted to go to bed.

Below there were only a few isolated lights. Tom climbed up into his bunk and slid in sideways. He pushed off his boots and stowed them alongside the duffel bag. He slept in his clothes, his feet jammed against the bag and was thankful he wasn't much taller.

The next morning the lights were turned on and lists of names were read, but mercifully there was little duty. Tom's name would not come up on the KP list. Most of the patrol and fire watch was done by the MPs.

He hurried to the latrine, the head, where he discovered the water in the wash basins and showers was salt and unheated. Brushing his teeth did not freshen his mouth and washing his face left it feeling sticky and oily.

Tom found the end of the chow line and learned the sleeping compartment would be closed from 8:00 AM to 6:00 PM during the day. Standing in line Tom felt a different motion to the ship, a kind of roll that, while not immediately noticeable, would cause the soldiers in the line, from time to time, to catch their balance. The chow hall was the same hell as before. The bread, coffee, and peach slice accompanied by powdered eggs this time.

But on deck Tom found his breath both restored and taken away by the beauty of the morning. A fresh, moist, cool breeze, the heavy vibration of the ship as it was truly under way, and enormous bow wave curling in looping, prancing, splashing beauty; while churning from the stern was a whitish, bluish trail that extended miles behind the ship.

There were soldiers leaning over all the rails, clustering in silence to contemplate the intense vibrant blue of the sea. Tom stood at the full limit of the bow leaning over to watch the ship slice into the sea throwing foam and spray into the wind. He marveled at the flying fish skipping over the surface like pebbles, and he felt an immense calm excitement that he was present to witness these things.

There were loudspeaker messages from time to time requesting certain officers to report to various places. There were announcements that the smoking lamp was out or was lit according to some unknown demands of the ship. The decks were ordered swept down fore and aft. Tom learned the latter meant he had a moment to scramble out of the way before details hosed down the deck to be followed by another group of men with brooms who swept the sea water into the scuppers.

As the morning went on small groups of men played cards or shot craps. Others napped and correspondents resumed writing letters to their sweethearts adding each day's letter to the previous ones that would be mailed when the opportunity came. Their writing desk stationary boxes on their knees, some soldiers read progressively more dog-eared paperbacks that, at first, had three or four, and later six or more people waiting to read it next; westerns or mysteries, mainly.

Others, to pass the time, chatted about food or girls they had known, or boasted of adventures involving lots to drink followed by mindless vandalism.

There was little speculation about what was to come despite frequent exhortations to take good care of your piece, because it might save your life someday. There were no referent experiences for the younger soldiers who had not been in World War II five years previously. There was only something unknown that was to happen to them, and it did little good to try to define or imagine it. Tom succeeded in disallowing any effect of speculation about the future of his behavior. Time was seen receding behind him as a road recedes. What would happen in the next five minutes, or months, was received as it occurred without anticipation or any observation of cause and effect. A road unfamiliar and untraveled. Around the next corner a vista of farmland and rivers, or a city, on a desert. A terrible traffic accident with bodies strewn among smoking wreckage, a fruit stand selling ice cold cherry cider. He might line up for a meal at the mess tent and be pulled out a moment before his mess kit was held out to the cook and be sent by truck 15 miles away to stand by the side of a road, or at some intersection of dusty tracks and wait there until he was picked up. Sometimes there was some sort of explanation, but these would rarely accord with what eventually transpired.

So, Tom concentrated on surviving physically in the moment and his psyche came wagging behind him. It went almost everywhere he went, even to Korea one day.

The midday sun was quite hot, but the men were under strict orders to keep their fatigue jackets buttoned and the sleeves rolled down. They were to wear fatigue caps as well. The Army had a positive aversion to sunburned troops and the men were told they would be punished if they evidenced any over— exposure to the sun. Tom sought what shade could be found in the overhangs and under the lifeboats and napped through the hot part of the day.

By noon Tom was hungry. By 3:00 the chow line had

been established for an hour, and it was almost 5:00 before Tom received, on a wet metal tray, the bread, butter, coffee and peach ration supplemented this time with a serving fork of sauerkraut and two wieners.

After dinner Tom hung around the passageways until the compartment was opened. He went down and lay on his bunk and listened to the complaints and triumphs of the crap shooters kneeling around a blanket in one corner of the compartment.

After a while Tom roused himself and took his dirty underwear and socks to the showers in the head near the stern. He stood under a stream of tepid sea water and scrubbed the clothing.

The bar of yellow soap he used merely filmed on the fabric in a sticky mess. Tom took the things to the sink and tried to scrape as much of the soap off of them as he could. He wrung them out and carried them back to his bunk where he draped them over the metal frame. The problem of washing clothes never was solved. Some soldiers secured lengths of line and tied their clothing to an end and flung the bundle over the stern thinking to perhaps drag their clothing clean, but the bundles skipped like stones, like flying fish, across the surface of the water; and they were drawn back up wet, but still smelly and sticky with oil, grease, soot, and salt. Tom's own fatigues grew glossy with a greasy substance, not dirt, but some nautical sea-going first cousin to dirt that was picked up by lying on the decks and hatch covers.

At night the troop ship showed no lights, but there were other ships to see in the distance and there were the stars, the number and luminosity of which he would never have believed. He lay on his back and gazed into the stars, and it seemed as if there was an immense depth he was looking into, that the rumbling, hissing, throbbing troop ship was embarked onto some voyage into the stars. He felt light-headed and far from the touch stones of daytime experiences. Lying with his body heavy against the tarpaulin covered hatch, he decided to let go, to reverse the polarities and let himself fall into space. He felt the rush of wind across his face for the few seconds he traversed the earth's troposphere; and then there was more of a sense of drifting downward although he would judge as rapid because of the large shifts in the location of the stars. He tried to calculate how far he would travel at this speed, probably less than that of light. He began to lose a feel for up and down, and he seemed not to be traveling; more or less sandwiched between layers of stars. Not so much downward as outward. He closed his eyes and returned to the vibrating hatch of the troop ship. That had been kind of fun.

The troop ship continued south, the decks were swept fore and aft, the canned peaches were replaced by canned pears for a meal or two, and on one unhappy breakfast canned Kadota figs and the flying fishes flew.

Father: Harold Sterns MacLean

Mother: Mary Anna Saunders MacLean

Brother: Robert Paul MacLean

1950

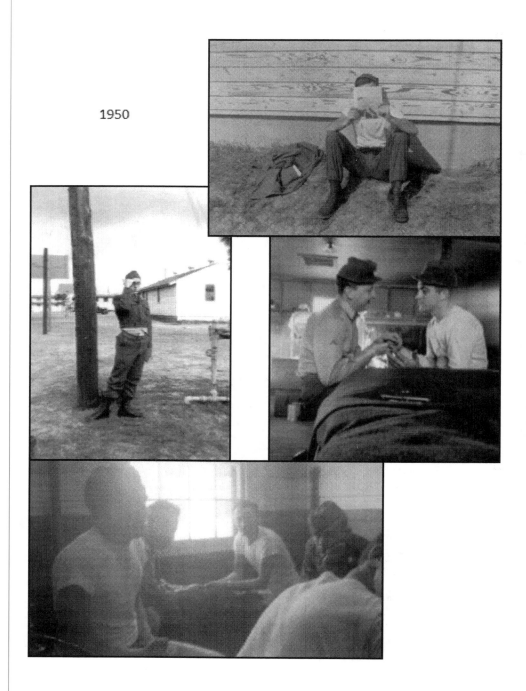

1951

1951

1951

1951

1952

1952

1952

OKLAHOMA

SERGEANT MAJOR'S AWARD

presented to

SERGEANT FIRST CLASS THOMAS F. MACLEAN

for perpetuating the traits and principles of leadership.
The professionalism you displayed reflects great credit upon
your unit and the non commissioned officers corps.

army national guard

September 1983
Date

State Command Sergeant Major

감사 서한
Letter of Appreciation

대 한 민 국
THE REPUBLIC OF KOREA

6·25전쟁 50주년
THE 50th ANNIVERSARY OF THE KOREAN WAR

존경하는 참전용사 귀하

　6·25전쟁이 발발한지 반세기를 맞아 세계의 자유 민주주의와 대한민국을 수호하는데 기여한 귀하에게 진심으로 감사드립니다. 아울러 고귀한 생명을 바치신 영령앞에 무한한 경의와 추모의 뜻을 표합니다.

　대한민국이 오늘날의 자유 민주주의 국가를 유지할 수 있도록 귀하께서 보여주셨던 불굴의 신념과 진정한 용기, 그리고 거룩한 희생정신을 우리는 가슴속 깊이 간직하고 있습니다.

　특히 귀하께서 50년전에 몸으로 실천했던 자유민주주의 이념은 이제 새로운 세기, 새 천년을 맞아 세계 인류의 보편적 가치가 되었습니다.

　이에 6·25전쟁 50주년을 맞이하여 귀하의 명예를 드높임과 동시에 과거 혈맹으로 맺어졌던 귀하와의 우의를 재다짐하고자 합니다. 아울러 인류의 발전과 평화를 위해 세계 우방들과 함께 노력해 나갈 것입니다.

　다시 한번 귀하의 숭고한 헌신에 깊이 감사드리며 행운과 건승을 기원합니다.

　감사합니다.

2000년 6월 25일

대 한 민 국 　대 통 령　　김 대 중

June 25, 2000

Dear Veteran

On the occasion of the 50th anniversary of the outbreak of the Korean War, I would like to offer you my deepest gratitude for your noble contribution to the efforts to safeguard the Republic of Korea and uphold liberal democracy around the world. At the same time, I remember with endless respect and affection those who sacrificed their lives for that cause.

We Koreans hold dear in our hearts the conviction, courage and spirit of sacrifice shown to us by such selfless friends as you, who enabled us to remain a free democratic nation.

The ideals of democracy, for which you were willing to sacrifice your all 50 years ago, have become universal values in this new century and millennium.

Half a century after the Korean War, we honor you and reaffirm our friendship, which helped to forge the blood alliance between our two countries. And we resolve once again to work with all friendly nations for the good of humankind and peace in the world.

I thank you once again for your noble sacrifice, and pray for your health and happiness.

Sincerely yours,

signed
Kim Dae-jung
President of the Republic of Korea

CHAPTER 13

One afternoon the troops noticed land to the west and then closer a tropical shore, and commercial and military installations. Then they learned that they were to transit the Panama Canal.

The vibration of the ship altered perceptibly, and the bow wave diminished as a grey pilot boat made its way toward the ship. The soldiers, all on their feet now, watching from the rail as khaki clad MSTS officers appeared and the civilian crew members prepared a boarding ladder. Orders were announced over the loudspeakers. Lines were tossed from the pilot boat and secured. The pilot boat swung in an arc and alongside and several men climbed to an open door in the side of the hull.

The ship resumed a bit of its previous speed and was met by tugs that were to accompany it to a dock bordered by vast aprons of concrete. There were low buildings and railroad tracks, dock workers sauntering or sitting and all looking up at the ship.

More buildings, trucks and pickups and farther back high chain link fences and groves of tropical vegetation.

As the ship was secured and long boarding ramps run out, Tom was surprised to hear that the soldiers would be allowed off the ship that evening to attend an outdoor movie at a ballpark in the area.

After dinner Tom joined the soldiers crowded in the

gangways and, then sure enough, chains were let down across the doors in the hull. Tom walked down a gangplank to feel the unfamiliar sensation of unmoving solid earth after the days of the subtle motion of the large ship making its way through calm seas.

Several thousand strolling soldiers moved in a sort of a column past the warehouses, through a section of barracks surrounded by green lawns to a regular old-fashioned wooden ballpark painted a dark green. Set up at the pitcher's mound was a large white screen.

And wonder of wonders, there was beer for sale and Tom drank a couple of the heavily dewed bottles in the mild tropical evening.

At dusk the movie began. Tom sat relaxed and happy and watched a Hollywood musical. He laughed and admired the cleanliness and grooming, and the wit and beauty of the performers. He even enjoyed the pauses when a fresh reel was put on and the anticipation of the resumption of the film.

And when it was time to wander back to the ship, he did so with the feeling that someone had done them a favor almost beyond gratitude. He'd even gotten a Panamanian quarter in his change when he'd bought beer and thought that would make a grand souvenir.

Reboarding the ship it seemed but a moment after re-entering that environment of metal and oil that the brief respite on shore had occurred in the distant past.

The next morning the ship was already locking a

section of the canal before Tom made it out from the vibration of the metal bulkheads, the rattle of the ventilation system, the sticky saltwater with which he rinsed his face and arms, the breakfast oatmeal. The morning was overcast and humid. Every inch of the deck was covered with soldiers watching the water rush into the enormous dripping locks, the ship moved to the next level, the donkey engines pull the ship into the next chamber.

It began to rain but there was so little difference in the feel of the humid air, sweat, and rain that few sought shelter and just stood in the steaming air.

The ship moved from the last lock in this series into a chain of enormous cuts made onto the red earth, the tops of the cuts were fringed with foliage of intense green. And then the rain let up as the ship moved into a great lake spotted with islands totally covered with tropical vegetation. The sun came out and clouds of vapor steamed off the decks and hatches, and wisps of vapor arose from the shoulders of the soaked men.

The locking through took all day, and it was dusk when the transit accomplished the ship tied up briefly at the Pacific end of the Canal. By this time Tom had seen all the Canal he wanted to.

The ship sailed into the Pacific, and Tom learned it was now bound for San Francisco to take on yet more troops for Japan. The ocean was a greenish—grey, not the intense blue of the Caribbean and as they went further north the wind stiffened and the ship began not only to roll but to pitch.

Standing in place in the chow line required the soldiers to brace themselves against losing their balance and the passageways became smelly and sticky with vomit.

Standing at a counter at dinner one afternoon a soldier opposite Tom coughed and then vomited splattering the boots and trousers of his neighbors. A KP came with a mop, smeared the vomit around and then rushed back to the galley.

Tom is on deck. The ship rolls so that at one point only the sky is visible from the railing, and then the ship rolls back and Tom is looking across vistas of pitching waves and curling spume. It grew colder and Tom sought his field jacket in his duffel bag. He sat in out of the way corners protected from the wind.

One morning land was visible to the east. Then a long line of white dunes, behind the dunes small pastel box-like houses. He was told it was San Francisco.

The ship sought a pilot boat and in a frenzy of pitching and throwing of wakes, a pilot boat makes it out to the ship. The channel was found, and the ship passed between the smooth red cliffs to the north and the mansions on the south, beneath the orange-red of the Golden Gate Bridge and its crawling toy cars, and into the Bay. Past the tall pines of the Presidio, Crissy Field, and Fort Mason where troops were already gathered to embark.

A brief lived rumor had it that they were to receive passes to visit the City there only a few hundred yards from the ship. But the ship tied up, the gangways were run down, the soldiers on the pier were boarded, and the gangways pulled up again almost in haste; as if it were feared the thousands of troops on board, 7,500, might collectively decide to go AWOL and in a mighty rush disappear, clambering aboard cable cars and taxi cabs, to scatter in the hills of San Francisco and in the hills beyond to play peek-a-boo in the Redwoods.

A few clusters of dock workers waved to them and the ship was backed out into the Bay, and the pilot was dropped literally into the pilot boat again and all that was over in the matter of only a few hours.

Tom was left with an impression of incredible neatness of the homes of the Marina district that bordered the fort and of the appearance of courtly courtesy of the traffic sliding up and down the hilly streets behind.

Headed west again into the Pacific, the pitching increased, and the ship buried its bow within a few yards of the railing and in doing so the screws came out of the water with a tremendous grinding shudder. At times the deck dropped from beneath Tom's feet. Hence walking was difficult and negotiating the stairs hazardous. Soldiers were injured in falls and carrying a tray of food in the mess became a half humorous ordeal. A tray of food in one hand, a canteen of coffee in the other, and even if Tom did manage to keep his balance the chance was that he would be bumped by someone else who lost his balance. The floor was slick with spilled food and wet with vomity mop water.

Some troops ill with seasickness simply skipped meals and quite a few began to suffer with boils ascribed to malnutrition.

The Band in the midst of the rolling, pitching, heaving seas, and now bitterly cold weather, was detailed to play twice daily concerts on one of the upper decks. Folding metal chairs were located, the Bandsmen unstacked their instrument cases. They played then twice a day a concert of some six or eight military marches while the wind whistled, and the spray wet the musicians and their audience.

The seas continued to increase until the decks ran with an inch or two of water that sloshed back and forth with the irregular laboring of the ship. The men were now permitted to stay below decks where most opted to brace themselves in their bunks clothed and wrapped in blankets. And, then the soldiers were ordered to stay below and were not permitted on deck.

It was as if the ship were placed in some abusive cement mixer with a violent random action. The movements were not predictable. Tom's efforts to balance himself were instantly defeated by the randomness of the sickening lurches, shudders, and slant of the heavily engaged vessel. The storm continued for a week.

Tom later learned that the ship was to have stopped at Hawaii to give the soldiers a break similar to the one at Panama, but that instead the ship had departed from its course by hundreds of miles in an attempt to avoid a typhoon.

The seas calm again, the course was more northerly than west, and the weather became crisp with a feel of ice in the air. Tom's days were now spent in napping and dozing. All the magazines and paperbacks had been read to pieces. A few books with missing pages still made their way around, crossword puzzle books had been solved, erased and solved again, all stories had been told, all fantasies related, all anticipations anticipated.

Tom often ate only once a day. He usually skipped breakfast. He washed in saltwater and rinsed his underwear. He preferred now to lie in his bunk rather than to sit on the metal deck or a hatch cover. Once a week he would stand in line and buy a carton of cigarettes from the ship's stores. The carton wrapped in brown waxed paper cost a dollar. For sale also were razor blades, after shave, toothpaste, soap. There was a wrist- watch or two and initially boxes of Ritz crackers, but those had been sold out even before Panama.

Four weeks after the ship left New Orleans, the soldiers spied low-green islands they were told were part of Japan. The ship passed between them. The sea became mercifully calm and the color of the intense blue of the Caribbean. The air was chilly, and the mountains of the larger islands were covered with snow. The sea was covered with jelly fish. They saw wooden fishing boats of moderate size and exotic design. The fishermen were squatting amid the nets on the decks and wore headbands of twisted cloth around their foreheads. They wore patched quilted jackets.

The troop ship continued north and picked up a destroyer escort. The novelty of this caused the men to stir around, to observe and comment and to go below to organize their gear.

On the morning of the 31st day aboard, the ship stopped outside the bay of a small grey port city built on the lower slope of a snowy mountain range. US Army tugboats with huge ropy bows, rows of tires along each side of their hills nudged the ship into the harbor crowded with fishing boats and small incredibly rusted coastal freighters.

Tom stared hard at the grey stucco warehouses with external tiles, pipes and bamboo scaffolding that was secured with braided straw ropes; at the dock workers wearing Japanese Army forage caps squatting around small braziers shoveling rice into their mouths from metal mess tins, at horse drawn freight wagons, banners, peculiar narrow gauge steam locomotives and their Japanese engineers and firemen, at the high-bodied boxcars and passenger cars. And masking the smell of the sea and seaweed came the dock smells, dry manurish, wood smoke, charcoal, outhouse smells that Tom was to smell in every small town and village while he was in the Orient.

There were Army vehicles, trucks, jeeps, and weapon carriers with the 45th Division designation on their bumpers and white stars on the doors and hoods. There were the three-wheel Japanese motorcycle pickups loaded with rice straw-covered cartons, and wooden tubs with rope handles. The drivers were young men who wore cast off Japanese and American uniforms and canvas topped shoes with a separation for the big toe.

Loudspeakers ordered the soldiers to their compartments where they readied their field packs and adjusted their rifle slings. They put on their steel helmets with the old chalked on numbers from New Orleans and secured the bunks and sat on their duffel bags awaiting their turn to disembark.

An hour or so of waiting and the Band Company, in turn, was called. Help was sought in putting on packs, and then they struggled up the stairs and through the hatch ways, and then out into the fresh cold air and down onto the pier while the dock workers squatted and smoked and watched.

They went through a warehouse door and down through the building to another door that exited onto a railroad platform where they all clambered aboard passenger cars that had wooden benches and silly little lamps and absurd square little windows. It was like a toy train. It whistled and puffed, and a Japanese brakeman and a conductor waved lanterns, and with a weak little bump the little train was moving through a rail yard grim with soot and cinders.

Again, Tom looked hard with a slight frown at the backs of buildings, at people, at the rail crossings waiting for the train to pass. Women in kimono with white aprons, white socks and zori, babies on their backs, children with Dutch boy haircuts, and older children somewhat gaunt and somewhat simian leaning on bicycle handlebars, or pushing carts, or pulling wagons and carrying packages knotted in scarves. Young women in western dress with high-heel shoes in anklets and wearing sweaters over their dresses. Commercial areas with goods for sale all hanging from the outside of the shops in enormous displays of pots and pans, or vegetables. Paper lanterns strung across the street alternating with rows of light bulbs. Loudspeakers wailing on each street corner. Tom stared hard and tried to remember everything he saw.

He wanted to return to these neighborhoods to see what was hidden by a bend in the street, what was further down the block. Someone said the name of the town was Otaru. The town was off limits because of the large number of Communists active there.

The train was soon in the country and hurrying in its own mild rocking way on an elevated roadbed through rice paddies and over bridges spanning rushing streams of clear water. There were rice straw-capped farm laborers plowing with oxen and farm families sitting in groups smoking or eating. Tom was struck by the incredible neatness and order of the farmland, and the clear delineation and specifically designated utility of the farm plots. This is definitely pasture, this is a rice paddy without question. The road begins here, and here the vegetable patch begins. A formal garden of a farmscape. In Oklahoma the fields ended in irregular, uncared for lines of weed filled ditches that bordered dirt roads half dirt and half weed.

Further past the flat land rice paddies were terraces of rice paddies, then forests up to the snow line. They passed small stations with the Japanese rail officials dressed in blue uniforms with brass buttons and billed caps with chrysanthemum badges.

Tom wondered what they thought of him, a soldier in the occupying Army; and, they, the citizens of a defeated nation. He wondered how difficult it was for them to accept defeat even though now they'd had almost five years to become accustomed to it. He wondered if he were hated like he was sure he would hate Japanese soldiers riding on a train through Bethany.

Despite the bright sun the air was cold and, and when the train pulled onto the siding at Camp Crawford and the men fell into formation, Tom was glad they were on the sheltered side of a building and was grateful for the reflected heat of the concrete platform.

Camp Crawford had been a military base, he was told, for young Japanese airmen. The barracks were low one-story brick buildings. As one entered there were two squad rooms on either side, a bay with room for 40 or so men, racks and shelves between the windows and at the far end the latrine, and showers, and a laundry sink of black slate.

It was an attractive camp. There were the rows of brick barracks trimmed in white with slate roofs. Wide drill fields and down at the railhead two-story frame buildings containing the post laundry, barber shop, and quartermaster stores.

After drawing linens, the Bandsmen were given the rest of the afternoon, the two or three hours before the evening meal, to explore the post, or settle themselves in the barracks if they wished.

Tom made up his bunk, found his least rumpled khakis in the bottom of his duffel bag, and after the first hot freshwater shower in a month, he reveled in the fresh cool crispness of the khakis and set out to find the PX.

The PX was in a large stone and frame building. The clerks were young Japanese women. Tom went to a cashier where he exchanged dollars for military script and then went to the snack bar to join some earlier arriviees in eating hamburgers and drinking milkshakes.

He went exploring through the PX looking at wristwatches and radios. He bought cigarettes, tinned cheddar cheese, a product of New Zealand, and crackers. Suddenly very tired, he walked back to the barracks where he lay down in his clothes and went to sleep. He awakened cold in the night and undressed and went back to sleep until morning.

General MacArthur was preparing for an abrupt departure from command.

The next morning at Company formation the Bandsmen shivered in the chill of an early spring Hokkaido day and learned they were to stick around the barracks but had no specific duties for the next day or so.

After breakfast Tom returned to the barracks and emptied his duffel bag and pack out onto his bunk and proceeded to GI all his clothing and equipment to rid it of the sea water and tarpaulin stickiness, and afterward he lay on his bunk, with the skin of his hands white and shriveled from the hot soapy water, and ate cheese and crackers.

That afternoon Tom was detailed with a dozen others to go with a truck to the railhead where the enormous pine crates last seen in Louisiana had been off-loaded and were making their way to an eventual reunion with the Band. Tom and the others muscled the crates onto the truck and thence to their new supply room. The tops and sides of the crates were removed and the gear they contained carried and stacked, and arranged at the direction of the supply sergeant, and then the empty crates were returned to the railhead.

The Band's routine was quickly established and as the Division was dispersed to several training areas in camp, or field locations, and to tent cities; so it was with the Band. Tom remained with half the Band staying at Camp Crawford. The other half of the Band was trucked to a tent city called Camp Chitose.

Entertainment units were reformed. Two jazz bands, one for the NCO Club, the other for the Officers' Club, a Dixieland combo for entertaining in the field and a country western group was formed under the direction of a fiddle player who, in civilian life had left the Rochester Symphony for the greater remuneration of the Spade Cooley Band. The musical units were organized, but the Bandsmen were not really assigned to any particular one. There was the core of professional musicians who eventually played most of the dances and shows, supplemented, or replaced on occasion by the younger less experienced Bandsmen, who performed chiefly with the military band.

These musicians had a very heavy schedule. The military bands played for formations almost every evening and for the battalion and regimental reviews on Saturday morning. The full band would reunite, not infrequently, to play concerts at the Camp Crawford post theater, or at concert halls and theaters in Sapporo for Japanese audiences. The program of one of these concerts might include a suite for the band, a soloist or two, a trumpet trio was always enthusiastically received. After an intermission, the band was formed into a male chorus and would sing short pieces from classical literature, a show tune, or medley, always ending with a rousing, THIS IS MY COUNTRY.

Rehearsals were intensive, and after morning details and housekeeping, and infantry drill, the afternoons were spent in section or ensemble practice with each Bandsman held responsible for his part which was played and criticized and practiced until it was satisfactory to the section leader.

The Division was now involved in large scale field training exercises coordinating armor, artillery, and infantry. The Bandsmen were an entertainment unit, but came to take themselves seriously as soldiers too, and continued independent platoon and company level training, individual weapons drill, bayonet drill, and, Tom's favorite, route marches of a day or half-day's duration along the country lanes and dirt roads that looped around the camp on dikes alongside rice paddies and dairies, and that went up and through the valleys of the surrounding hills and mountains. On days not structured by specific Band duties or training all the Bandsmen not assigned the usual housekeeping duties would fall into formation dressed in fatigues with webbed belt and canteens, ponchos folded and riding on their butts tucked through the back of the webbed belt. One of the officers would march them out the gate into the surrounding country.

During each hour's ten minute break Tom would sit on his helmet and smoke and watch the farmers, or the flow of water over the stones of a stream until it was time to march again.

The first weeks in Japan the soldiers were not allowed passes into town. There was talk of Communist agitation. But many of the Bandsmen reconnoitered the scattered rural settlements outside the perimeter of the post and returned to share their intelligence. In particular, one acquaintance of Tom's went almost every evening to a small farmhouse built near the bed of a wide river a half mile or so from the post gate. He made friends with the family to whom he took whatever PX items the family requested or occurred to him to take to them. He told Tom he sat around the family's charcoal braizer drinking tea or beer and eating from various dishes the family prepared and communicating, but not conversing, as they spoke in Japanese, and he in English.

Tom's own first hands-on-experience with the Japanese, other than brief transactions at the PX snack bar or over the counter purchases of cigarettes, canned cheese and crackers, came about on a Saturday afternoon when he went to the post barber shop and found all the barbers were Japanese girls.

These girls weren't rice powdered geisha, but stocky, round-faced, ruddy-cheeked farm girls who cut hair with comb and scissors. It was a novel experience and not unpleasant to have a bosom lean into his shoulder while the barber snipped cozily away. The conversation was limited to lively, 'You like?' and other short phrases. To Tom's surprise, which rapidly became full-blown embarrassment, the regular full service haircut included having his face, nose, forehead, and neck examined for blackheads and pimples which the barbarette extracted, or at minimum disturbed by squeezing the matter between the finger-nails of her pointer fingers. The feeling of violation was as intense as his shame. Then came the intensely musky hair oil, a product of Japan, a dusting of powder, and his 35 cent haircut was complete.

Back at the barracks Tom washed the oil and snippets of hair from his scalp and resolved to have a good going over of his own at the mirror before going to the barber shop again.

And now before long Tom will encounter Sapporo, the bridge, the swimming pool, the bars and restaurants, the downtown EM Club, sweet bean filled pastries, charcoal fired taxis, fish canneries, rental row boats, the university, black market streets, canned octopus, pro kits, Otaru again, skiing children, quonset huts, CIC, snow, Atami, Tokyo, trains, and ferries, pup tents and shelter halves, swimming, picnicking, snakes in bamboo cages, promotions, the Meiji Palace, pachinko, geta, pedicabs, mud, manure, roasted corn, beer, rare old Nikka liquor, football games, and cheerleaders from Division Headquarters.

CHAPTER 14

In freshly scrubbed, starched, and ironed khakis, low cuts shined to a mirror finish, blue-braided field cap cocked forward resting just above the bridge of his nose, web belt scrubbed almost white, buckle polished to a creamy brass, a fresh pack of Camels, a sheaf of 100 yen notes, Tom sat half at attention on the edge of the seat in a bus to town. He looked at the edges of town and finally the countrified city streets of Sapporo a city of several hundred thousand Japanese souls, the commercial center of Hokkaido, Japan's northernmost big island home of the Ainu, who tattooed their women's faces and hunted bear, north of Vladivostok and west of Oklahoma City.

It was Tom's plan to dine at the EM Club and then explore the city by night. The only constraint or obligation was to return to the post by midnight. Otherwise Tom's visit and activities would be limited only by the boundaries imposed by his own audacity, discretion, or timidity.

The EM Club in Sapporo provided drink, food, and entertainment to any soldier and invited guest in a decent and dignified fashion. The primary meal served was steak, potatoes, peas, and a lettuce salad. It was adequate, nutritious, and fresh. On the other hand the meals at the post, because of some supply regulation, were composed of foods shipped frozen, canned, or dried from the United States.

The beverages at the club were milk, Coke, and beer.

During the week there was dancing to a jukebox and on the weekend a Band unit played if it was available or music was provided by the Swing Stars, a trio of middle-aged Japanese who with their best efforts met an aching need to be filled in 1951 with as much success as a group of Oklahoma western swing shin kickers could, who assumed the responsibility for filling in at a Kabuki theater on odd nights, temporarily abandoning their steel guitars, fiddles, and saxophone for the kotos, gongs, and whatever else makes a Kabuki go.

The Swing Stars wore Hawaiian shirts, read from charts copied from fake books obtained when or where and felt comfortable in their roles and looked up from their music stands only when it came time, several times, in the course of an evening, at least once each set, to play their own memorized arrangement of Buttons and Bows.

After dinner Tom paused at the top of the steps of the entrance of the EM Club and then walked to the right where the lights seemed brighter and the crowds seemed thicker. By this time in the evening the main stores were closed, but the small stands on the curb side of the sidewalk remained open to feed the apparently insatiable Japanese windowless shoppers' interest in copy books, magazines, gadgets and items made of tin, thread, tissue paper, rayon, or bamboo, and any combination of these basic building blocks.

Tom was enormously interested himself but feigned inattention after a while because a moment's pause immediately summoned forth a casual, "Hey, GI. You want?" This spoken almost without fail by a natty young Japanese male with a wickedly knowing leer acknowledging

Tom's presumed depravity and flourishing a cigarette held in a short cardboard cigarette holder.

Tom would be openly curious only when surrounded by a crowd of decent wholesome Japanese infants or elderly honestly engaged in whatever was commonplace, and then having abandoned his brisk gait for a moment to regard more closely some item, a pimp would materialize smiling an awful smile and sucking air politely through his teeth while waiting for some response to his pro-positions.

And thus, Tom strode purposefully from one end of the nighttime business district to the other and through alleys that crisscrossed the main streets, and he took in impressions of weathered wood, gauze banners of red, yellow, or blue with enormous Japanese characters printed on them. Dull yellow light bulbs, the musky smell of charcoal and manure, women in dark kimonos and geta, men in dark pants, jackets, and rubber boots, music from street corner loud speakers punctuated with gongs and clacks, thumps and nasal expletives.

Tom took the 11:30 bus back to the post sharing it with several others as pensive as he and two drunks fortunate to be shepherded by solicitous buddies.

That was the first of uncounted excursions into town because unlike Louisiana which was a humid cousin of Oklahoma and whose charms went for the most part unencountered, Japan was an unending source of novelty and fascination. For example, a crowd is gathered at an intersection. Thanks to Tom's Yankee height he sees easily over the heads of the standees and bicycle riders, the school children and the elderly to a table. On one end of the table is a bamboo cage, elaborate, cunningly designed with a resident finch, plump and cheerful. On the other end of this table is a miniature temple, many steps, carved, gilt, exotic. One of the throng gives a small coin or folded currency to the guardian of the show. The cage door is opened, the bird flutters across the table to the temple steps, hops up to the temple door and selects with its beak a card from an assortment there, and then the guardian lady takes the card from the bird's beak as all crush around to see and hear and once the bird is in the cage again the consumer's fortune is read from the card. And more coins are preferred, and comments made and currents in the crowd are generated by those whose curiosity is sated, and who push to the outside and by those who push closer through the onlookers to get within arm's reach of the fortune telling apparatus.

Sometimes Tom went to town with Bandsmen whose interests lay in whorehouses they particularly favored and made them their EM Club in town where they'd eat and hang around. Initially Tom was quite cautious, the effect of six month's VD films and lectures having made their seemingly indelible impression, that was, the primary argument especially that the disease agents could lurk asymptomatic for as many as 20 years in his spinal column juices and then in a fever of activity, Rip Van Winkle like, could infect his wife of the future and ravage himself as well.

Tom's first visit then to his friend's whorehouse club

involved a cautious and clinical approach with condom, minimal physical contact other than rubber clad genital, a tube of antisomething with the rough metal tip squeezed into his urethra, washing of the genital area, and the sober reflection that all that really wasn't worth it.

Gradually over the weeks, familiarity lessened Tom's anxiety and most and sometimes all of the precautions were discarded.

The VD rate was reassuringly low because of the vigorous government program of frequent examinations of the prostitutes. It wasn't unheard of for a soldier to contact VD, but it was uncommon among the soldiers who went to sober, wholesome, regulated whorehouses and who avoided the dingy and pathetic street walkers.

CHAPTER 15

Once Tom was wandering afield through a residential neighborhood with a comrade when they were attracted to the gate of a large school by the sound of rather disciplined cheering and large crowd enthusiasm. They walked into a large central area playing field size and discovered athletic events, banners, a stage with festive decorations and hundreds of school children and adult spectators.

The student athletes were a quite determined bunch wearing sneakers, floppy wide-legged running shorts, little undershirts with numbers pinned to them and knotted headbands. All had stringy legs and narrow chests. Tom watched from the sidelines and then an adult with a great smiling manner punctuating his politeness with the now familiar hissing interdental inhalations beckoned and urged and waved Tom and his friend to the stage at the head of the activities where they were introduced and shook many hands and sat in folding chairs.

And later with gestures of his own Tom was obliged to hand out ribbons and handshakes to the children athletes. Tom in turn was presented with a composition book with many thanks and bows and further gestures until he smiled and pointed to his watch and gestured and departed turning with many waves and smiles until he had left the multitude.

Now a word about the buying habits of the American soldiers wherein tons of goods were purchased, taken to the

PX for car-toning, boxing, or crating in really very nice pine boxes sometimes and sometimes wrapped in sturdy brown paper and tied with heavy twine and sent via air mail or by sea to North America. The soldiers sent vases of metal or porcelain decorated often with cranes nosing around in bamboo, knives with leather sheathes and handles carved from bone or of formed plastic with dragons on them, pool cues that came apart and fishing rod sets that fit inside long boxes of pine, rayon jackets usually black with tigers or dragons embroidered on them, paintings of the surf in moonlight, again tigers, dragons and such-like on black velvet. Carved ivory or bone chess sets, ceramic figurines, sets of dishes service for 12, tea pots, jewelry, these a partial listing of the stuff sent home.

For their use in the barracks the soldiers bought men's kimonos, geta for use as shower shoes, elaborately shaped cigarette holders, lighters of incredibly inferior craftsmanship, strange iron bladed cleavers and tools that came in handy for digging and chopping when they were in the field. Some bought snakes in bamboo cages which they kept as pets. One soldier panicked when his two-foot-long pet, whom he was used to draping over his shoulder while playing cards, took a turn or two around his neck one evening, squeezed, and his master slightly squeamish even though familiar enough after the couple of week's ownership, clawed at his pet, who in turn really clamped down. The master fearing snake bite or asphyxiation gave rein to his previously suppressed slight revulsion during the few weeks of their relationship, leaped to his feet and ran from the barracks uttering gargled screams.

Once the pet was removed from his neck by his companions who caught the card player in the company street and sat on him to effect the removal he put it back in its cage and took it to a bushy area at the edge of the post. He turned all its snakiness loose and relinquished it and the attention and the slight reputation for eccentricity he had enjoyed for a while.

Tom made the acquaintance late one afternoon of the first of the three girlfriends he was to have in Japan when he stopped for a beer at a small restaurant. He sat at the end of a counter and when served Tom noticed what appealing mannerisms the girl had. Tom eventually ordered another bottle and this time the girl asked him why he was so sad, a conversational gambit encountered for the first time. Tom assured her he wasn't sad and after an exchange with her very limited English he asked her when she would be off work and where she lived. She said she didn't work Sunday and that she lived with her parents in a large apartment complex nearby, but that it would be awkward because her parents were adamant, she should have nothing to do with American soldiers. This advice I might add I concur in wholeheartedly and would give to my own daughters if I had any in these circumstances because you never know.

The next Sunday afternoon Tom went to the apartment complex and asked two youngsters if they knew Toshiko. He gave them chewing gum and promised them more if they'd let her know he was waiting there for her.

A little later she appeared only slightly less pretty than he'd remembered, and they took a walk around a lake and sat on a bench. He remarked how soft her shoulder was and to his mortification she said his shoulder was nice and soft too. She bought some kind of crunchy snack which they shared composed of soy flavored seaweed. She said she had to go back home because her parents were waiting. That was the end of their first date.

On their next date they went to the picture show. Some townspeople stared at them and muttered comments, but Toshiko was bright and cheerful and held his arm closely anyway. Tom did enjoy being with her, but her English was limited, and he had no delight in or enthusiasm for teaching her new words or correcting her pronunciation. Thus, she said pretty much the same things over and over, "You like? Never Happen."

Once they went boating in a rental rowboat, a monstrously heavy wooden affair. When she caught his eye, she would smile and sigh pleasantly. Tom got tired of that. Sometimes she would have small presents for him when they met. She said her parents were upset with her but that she liked him very much and could put up with her parents' angry disapproval.

Once or twice Tom was late and felt bad about it especially when Toshiko acted so happy and relieved and she asked for reassurance that everything was all right.

They had kissed and petted but Tom didn't find her appealing after all. He didn't like the heavy sweet scent of her hair. He learned she was 24. He just quit going to see her. He stayed away from her section of town.

Eating dinner once at the EM Club he saw her standing at the dining room entrance. Girls were permitted in the lobby to wait for their soldier friends but were not permitted unaccompanied into any of the other rooms at the Club. She was wearing a familiar coat with a fur collar. She waved and he turned away. When he glanced back, she was gone. She was a very nice girl.

The route marches continued through the countryside. The days were long and hot. Now the Band was to bivouac for a week. They were burdened with the unfamiliar full packs with all their crossing and snapping together of webbing and straps. They walked through pastures and on paths traversing rice paddies and then the CO took a fancy to jogging for a while, he without a pack, and the men's and boy's canteens and packs and weapons jostled and slipped causing exclamations of anger and fatigue. And then the line of struggling soldiers was to run up a hill.

Tom was near the end of the column, so he had to run several hundred yards before he even reached the hill trail, overgrown, wet and slippery. By the time Tom reached the top and was allowed to collapse the CO was brightly insulting the late-comers and contrasting his age and fitness with their callowness and lack of stamina.

When they reached the bivouac area, they found it to be a wide grassy gently sloping rise with a view of the countryside. Their bivouac neighbors to whom they were attached for meals had already arrived by truck, set up squad tents for the clerks and cooks, had dug and set up canvas walls around the officers' and EM latrines. The Bandsmen enjoyed setting up their pup tents.

You chose a buddy with whom to snap your shelter half thus completing the tent for two. You discussed drainage problems, aesthetics, and so on. After the tent was erected ditches to carry away draining rainwater were scratched with entrenching tools, a beer sump was dug in the far end of the tent and any cans of beer that had been packed along were deposited in the cool moist earth. Extensions in the form of front porches were rigged from extra ponchos or shelter halves.

It was pleasant if the job was well done to sit snug and dry in the tent while it rained and to have yourself and all your gear protected.

There had to be rules about where to remove your boots before crawling into the sleeping quarters of the tent proper and understandings about where things were to be stored. It was real cooperative housing and in the undemanding routine of the bivouac it was kind of fun. When the weather was good, they ate their meals seated on the grass in conversation circles of various sizes. When it was raining, they retreated to their tents and ate lying on their stomachs, propped on their elbows ever alert to weak points in their drainage ditch defenses.

The week of squad tactics passed quickly at the

bivouac. They investigated more of the hilly terrain of Hokkaido and then were trucked back to Camp Crawford courtesy of their Quarter-master Company hosts.

Once Tom visited the other Band half, designated B Band, at their tent city at Chitose. B Band was way out in the country. With no nearby towns their social life had degenerated to drinking beer in the PX tent and roasting ears of field corn purchased or stolen from the adjacent farms. There were outdoor movies occasionally, but the soldiers could have been in North Dakota or Louisiana as far as the variety of their experiences that were limited by their isolation. B Band had spent a lot of time gathering stones from a river and placing them to outline the Company walkways, each stone white-washed. What a way to spend one's time, but they were a common feature of the Army squad tent villages.

The afternoon Tom was at Chitose he walked down to the river with his friends, a mountain stream really, took off his dusty clothes, and waded to the middle of the stream where he crouched with his back to the current in the waist-high water and shouted his disbelief at how cold it was. He dried off in the sun and then back at Chitose said goodbye and left in the truck that daily brought mail and ferried other necessities from Camp Crawford.

Some of the Bandsmen had developed regular routines when given time off. Some took to regular visits to small towns an hour or so away from Sapporo on railway lines, towns that supposedly were off limits to enlisted men and reserved for officers, or as in the instance of Otaru, off limits to all military personnel who had no specific business there.

Once Tom accompanied a friend to a small resort village in the mountains. It consisted of maybe three large hotels in a mountain gorge. Below the hotels was a mountain torrent and across the stream a few steep streets of shops garlanded with lanterns and streamers. Tom was nervous about going there, especially as there were a half dozen officers on the train and no other GIs. He feared some kind of trouble with the MPs or the embarrassment of a reprimand from one of the officers, but after obtaining reassurance from his friend Tom settled back to watch the countryside as the train climbed through spectacular switch backs.

At the cold grey train station Tom and his friend and the officers left the train, the officers not so much glancing at them, perhaps indifference, perhaps recognizing it would serve no purpose to harass a couple of inoffensive GIs.

Tom's friend said that he spent most of his time in one or two modest restaurants at a table or booth near the rear and that was the way he remained unobtrusive. He stayed away from the places popularly frequented by the officers and in turn was treated to a quiet weekend uninterrupted by the noise and fights of the places the EM congregated in Sapporo.

A cold mist hung low over the village site, really a ravine where the resort had been built over thermal mineral springs. The streets were clean and quiet. They ate lunch at a small restaurant and drank beer seated in the corner of a deck that overlooked the stream, here a series of rapids, and over to a resort hotel all steamy windows on the ground floor where the baths and spas were.

Late in the afternoon they walked across a stone bridge to that hotel and Tom's friend made arrangements for baths and rub downs. Again, to Tom's surprise no one objected to their enlisted men's status, there was no embarrassment or rude refusal.

In a room off the bathing room Tom undressed and his clothing was neatly folded by an attendant. He was given a miniscule towel of rough cotton cloth and he walked nude to a large indoor pool. There was a misty vision of the ravine and river through moist windows that extended from floor to ceiling. On the wet tile floor were scattered wooden stools and wooden buckets. His friend showed Tom how they were to dip water from the pool and then carefully wash and rinse before entering the pool. The water was hot. They joined three or four Japanese gentlemen who were already soaking. Perspiration broke out on Tom's forehead and he told his friend that he didn't know how long he'd be able to take the hot water. His friend told him there were two smaller pools of even hotter water, one really just a tub, that few bathers even among the Japanese submitted to.

Finally, a sensation of suffocatingly wet cotton in his nose and throat drove Tom from the pool and he walked now shriveled red and white to a massage room where a masseuse and her aide assisted him in toweling dry. He climbed to lie face down on a table covered with a light pad.

Tom felt a liberal application of powder and then the masseuse using the palms of her hands and the tips of her fingers massaged and pressed and pulled Tom into a delightful state of helpless relaxation. In 10 minutes, Tom felt literally as if he had no bones or muscles but consisted entirely of some plastic dough-like tissue.

Tom was then left alone in this state for a half hour's doze and then an attendant appeared with a heavy cotton kimono and a bottle of beer. Very carefully Tom broke the pleasure of relaxation and sat up to drink the beer.

Tom and his friend dressed and left the hotel where outside the cool moisture cut into his damp scalp and he marveled at the sense of total physical cleanness. He felt his legs moving under the starched khaki trousers and his arms under the sleeves of his shirt.

Once Tom went to Sapporo on a Saturday morning and decided to walk back to camp as the program for that day's excursion. As Tom walked along a country road, he began to ease the restrictions he'd imposed on himself by which he did not permit himself to reflect on his parents' deaths, or what might lie ahead for himself once out of the Army.

Tom reached the river bridge which lay before the camp and mid-span in his mind's eye he jumped to his death and joined his parents in heaven. Tom looked into the sky over the mountains on the horizon and believed his parents were watching and aware of his thoughts. He stood motionless for half-an-hour but in his imagination he climbed the railing of the bridge, let go falling backward, experienced the aching sense of fear and loss in his stomach and chest, landed on his back in the rocks with an immense annihilation of his consciousness and life.

Tom very quietly and dispassionately repeated the process and each time it was the same. He was standing facing out from the bridge holding onto the cold metal railing. He would hear his breathing louder and louder. He would step over the railing open his hands and fall backward. For just a moment he would fall, eyes squeezed in a grimace and then the destroying blow against the back of his head and shoulder.

Tom would climb over the railing and move to where there was no bridge structure beneath him, only the rocks of the river. He would breathe slowly and steadily and the breath would sound louder and louder in his ears and then he would lean back and open his hands and would fall with his eyes squeezed shut in this state of gripping inevitability, and then his body with its consciousness would be dashed on the rocks and he would be dead. Finally, Tom lighted a cigarette and finished his walk back to camp.

CHAPTER 16

The Army for reasons best known to itself had a program of rest and recreation tours intended to better the morale of the troops that was offered even to the Bandsmen stationed in the country club environment of Camp Crawford. A certain number of men were permitted a week's leave, were given travel and hotel vouchers and were sent on their merry ways. One such opportunity arose for which there was little competition to be the one selected perhaps because of the distance and the days spent in travel, or it was close to payday and there was little discretionary income. The leave was to a resort town south of Tokyo, Atami. When Tom was offered a chance, he said he'd like to go and the orders were cut. He was given a half-inch sheaf of mimeographed papers.

Tom washed all his clothing, starched and pressed his spare khakis and the next morning made his way to the Sapporo train station where he followed some soldiers present and boarded a car half filled with other members of the 45th and other Army units headed for their various R&R destinations.

Tom didn't really know where he was going. Atami was just a name. He wasn't sure how long the trip would take. He went to sleep until he was awakened by a soldier who shook his shoulder and told him they were to leave the train and board a ferry to cross to Honshu.

He stood on an upper deck of the ferry leaning on a

railing looking at the deep blue of the strait. There were many fishing boats and boat traffic of other kinds. The surface of the water was thick with jellyfish and weeds. A soldier said there was food being served in the dining room and Tom was seated alone and fed an elaborate meal of several courses. He was interested in the substantiality of the dining silver and the coffee service.

They reboarded the train on Honshu and Tom sat and watched the grey wood and cinders of the city left behind and the green musky landscape under cultivation and then the hills and ravines.

He slept again, was awakened and ate in the dining car. Again, a very substantial meal, white linen, elaborate dining services. A bed was made up for him. He slept until the train reached Tokyo early the next morning. The train was in some kind of underground tunnel with tile walls. Tom dressed and remained on the train until the conductor told him that this train went no farther. He took his duffel bag and stood on the platform for a while. He wasn't bewildered or concerned, he just watched as people came and went and the train on which he'd arrived, now empty, went away somewhere.

Finally, he went to a window and handed the clerk his papers. He stood waiting while the clerk consulted other clerks and made a phone call and handed the papers on to yet another clerk. A blue uniformed official beckoned and Tom walked through a waiting room to another platform and a waiting train. His sheaf of papers was returned and the official left. Tom boarded the train and was glad to sit down.

He wished he had something to read. Back at camp he'd managed to read a few books. He had a copy of Don Quixote, and he'd borrow whatever was making its way around the barracks. Once he'd gotten a hold of a copy of Nostradamus and read sections of it feeling rather self-consciously important to be reading a book of what he assumed to be of more intellectual importance than the cowboy thrillers that were his usual fare. One afternoon a small group of Bandsmen were accompanying the Assistant CO on some errand or other and Tom alluded to some prediction of Nostradamus. The Assistant CO standing a short distance away laughingly asked Tom to repeat what he'd said. He was curious what Tom might glean from such a book. And so what Tom had interjected into a conversation with a kind of sly pride in his erudition, he now repeated embarrassed and patronized. Tom was resentful and shamed by the reaction to his slight performance this puppy - walking a few steps on its hind legs, a seal balancing a ball and slapping its flippers, a 17-year-old with intellectual pretensions.

A final bust of Japanese on the loudspeaker and this train moved off. Tom saw no other GIs on the train. He showed the papers to the conductor who looked noncommittal but after Tom had repeated the word Atami several times the conductor nodded and used the word Atami several times in the course of his response, nodded again and left. After an hour or so the conductor reappeared and said, "Atami, Atami," and gestured to Tom to take his duffel bag and prepare to disembark at the next stop.

And now he was in Atami. A small train station similar to the hundred or more his trains had passed in the last day and a half. The area is wooded. He catches glimpses of roofs and the sea farther below. Tom found a taxi parked around the corner of the station and reading the name of the hotel from the travel orders the cab driver nodded his recognition of Tom's destination.

They drove through a residential section then through deep woods. Here the curved road was flanked by terraces supported by enormous blocks of grey granite. Then through a gate into what Tom at first thought was the estate of a wealthy family, a garden of intense neatness and order, black pines, perfect lawns, and then under the overhang before the main entrance of the hotel, again a building more residential than commercial. One wing overlooked an expanse of lawn, then cliffs and the ocean. Tom was taken aback by the magnificence and grandeur of the hotel and its environs.

Tom paid the cab driver with a couple of the big 100 yen notes and entered the lobby. At the desk he presented his sheaf of papers to a smiling clerk who took them courteously and who after a cursory glance looked more carefully as if looking for something missed during the first riffle through the set of papers. The clerk asked Tom if perhaps he had other papers he could show, but Tom replied that those were all that he had been given. So, nodding, the clerk went to the manager's office where he conferred with a supervisor who then appeared and told Tom a key document was missing from the papers, specifically the hotel voucher, and that all rooms were allocated, there were no spare rooms. Some mistake had occurred.

And then as disappointment, the first emotion, the vanguard of the others that he was sure would follow seized him, the manager continued that however they would put a cot in the foyer of one of the suites and Tom was told that he would be quite comfortable. Why they should accommodate him thus Tom had no idea.

He followed the first clerk to a second floor suite and on the way upstairs the clerk issued orders to several maids and a porter and while Tom stood by in the foyer leading to a larger room a steel cot was set up and arranged and then turned cross-ways. The maids hastened to make the bed and bring extra blankets and more towels. And when all was prepared the clerk invited him to enjoy himself. He told him the times meals would be served in the dining room which was in the wing he may have noticed with the floor to ceiling French doors and the view of the ocean.

Tom took off his shoes and lay on the cot which was soft and clean. He roused himself to shower and shave. As he was taking his clothing from the duffel bag to hang in the closet the two soldiers whose suite he shared came in and said, "Hello." Tom recognized them from the first day on the train in Hokkaido. Perhaps they had stolen his voucher while he slept and pre-empted his rightful place in the bed by the balcony. His night table, his night lamp, his sense of being in the right place instead of on a cot in a foyer. But he was hungry for dinner, and he wanted to see Atami and drink some beer.

The dining room was immense. Many tables covered with snowy linen, mirrored walls, deep toned polished parquet floor. There were no more than three or four tables occupied by soldiers talking quietly. Tom sat alone at a table for four looking through the French doors to the lawn and the ocean. He had clear soup, crusty rolls with butter that had a taste of farm to it, green salad, roast pork, pan roasted potatoes, and peas. He drank milk. There was cake for dessert, moist with a heavy icing quite unlike the soy bean paste sweets he'd encountered in the Japanese pastry shops.

Despite the rural aspect of the surroundings, and he had wondered how far the hotel was from town, the entertainment district of Atami was adjacent to the near side of the hotel grounds and after dinner Tom walked through the side garden to a pedestrian gate that connected the hotel grounds with the steep cobblestone street divided by a rushing stream contained within a mortared channel.

The small hotels, bars, and restaurants, three stories or less, were all faced with bamboo. The wooden frame structures were exposed and varnished. The interior walls were rice paper covered screens. Lanterns and banners abounded as did music and twinkling lights. This was the red light district, houses of prostitution of a more elegant and light-hearted sort than he had seen before. It wasn't grim or furtive. There was lots of laughter and entertainment and the women stayed in the bars and hotels instead of soliciting on the street. There were no pimps or desperate offers to buy American cigarettes or currency. Tom strolled up and down the streets enjoying the sights and the cleanliness, the sounds of the stream rushing over rocks, the clatter of geta on the cobblestones. He sat on a stone bench as it grew dark and smoked cigarettes and watched the passersby, the coming and going of the men in the bars and hotels. The men wore the kimonos of their respective hotels, each a distinctive design in grey or dark blue with Japanese characters on the lapels or back. Subsequently, Tom would find a kimono from his own hotel on his cot and he'd wear it feeling oddly civilian on an evening stroll through town.

He saw but a few soldiers on these streets and learned in the course of a short conversation in the dining room that the GI hangout was a second story dance hall somewhat removed from the entertainment district. It was an American style bar with booths. The girls there spoke fairly adequate English.

He walked over there the second evening, but the drinking crowd was way ahead of him by the time he got there. They'd been at it three or four hours and the obscenities, the noise level, the scattered challenges, and scuffling didn't alarm him, but rather embarrassed him. He felt more allied with the sober bartenders and hostesses who had the problem now of maintaining some kind of order to minimize property damage and personal injury to their clients. There was all the interceding, cajoling, smiling, helping, and other duties attendant on managing drunks. The employees nodded agreeably and were shoved around as they held onto the arms of the drunks who lurched around and got sick and passed out or demanded more beer and mumbled long intense stories about loved ones and gooks and so on.

It was not a bad place really but by now the club was down to its last 10 drunks and the staff was appealing to the drunks' comrades to take them home or someplace else so that they could close up. A few drunks were amorous, but the hostesses could see they were dim prospects for any kind of deal. So, the drunks were poked and prodded. Tom left while the persistent few were still quarreling deep in their throats. He had often been a participant in the kind of scene he'd just witnessed, staggering, laughing, bawling out nonsense with the best of them.

He walked back through the quiet streets to his hotel. He thought briefly of going to a house of prostitution, but it was late and he would just as soon sleep. Not so his roommates. They didn't sleep in the hotel any of the three nights of their stay. Tom saw them once or twice when they came back to shave or change clothes, but they didn't sleep there. Tom slept until 10 and ate breakfast alone in the hotel dining room while the busboys set the tables for lunch.

After breakfast he walked down to the pebbly beach and inspected the wooden fishing boats pulled up above the reach of the surf or the tide. There were boat houses and associated commercial enterprises all shipshape and substantial looking. Tom walked past a lifeboat station with boats on slides ready to be rushed to the water and past fish processing buildings reeking of sharp marine smells.

He passed the beach to the market district of the town and looked at the fish stalls with wooden buckets of minnow-sized fish, octopus hung as if on clothes lines all moist and handsome but smelling to high heaven of yesterday's fish juices, past bundles of green vegetables, bundles of foot-long white radishes, more wooden buckets of salted and pickled vegetables, and ranks of sake bottles, and myriads of plastic household items.

By the time Tom had made his circuit which included the entertainment district again, maids tossing buckets of water to scrub the tile and stone entries, baskets of empty beer bottles collected and beer and sake delivered in three-wheeled pickups, by the time he had made this circuit it was time for lunch at the hotel.

Lunch was a meal indistinguishable from dinner. There were the same courses of soup and meat, many dishes brought and removed. And then after smoking a cigarette in the lobby he went upstairs to the suite where he slept away the rest of the afternoon. He awakened slightly puzzled as to the time. The sky was a dark grey. Perhaps he had slept through the night. He had no watch. He bathed and dressed and went down to the lobby feeling rested but strangely disassociated from the flow of time and eager to orient himself with the clock. It was 4:00 in the afternoon. A clerk was bent over papers and forms, a porter was emptying ashtrays, the dining room crew was unfolding fresh table linens and carrying trays of silverware in from the kitchen. Tom bought a carton of cigarettes from the desk clerk who took them from a special locked cabinet. He returned to his room and sat looking out the window and smoking cigarettes until time for dinner.

That evening Tom dressed in the hotel kimono and wore geta to walk in the entertainment district. He drank beer in a small bar. His hostess spoke no English but poured his beer, lighted his cigarettes, fetched snacks, folded paper birds out of 100 yen notes, smiled, and submitted to Tom's scrutiny. She wore a kimono. He liked that. Her hair was scented with the heavy muskiness he found distasteful. She had a gold tooth, her hair was coarse, her lipstick heavily applied. It was to be a platonic relationship. When she offered to pour beer into his already filled glass Tom realized she felt an obligation to her employer to speed up Tom's rate of drinking. He smiled and motioned for her to allow him out of the booth and she complied until she realized he was headed for the street rather than the toilet. She held onto his arm and smiled and pointed and cajoled and in dire professional need hazarded the first English, "Why you go?" Tom smiled tightly and then not at all and pushed past the hostess and decided that was enough conviviality for one evening. He went back to the hotel and lay awake a long time smoking in bed and not thinking of much.

The next morning, he was full of much unexpended energy and briskly walked the length of the beach and walked all through the residential districts and the market district. He walked out past the town and followed the shoreline climbing the rocks and examining the tide pools.

He made it back quite late for lunch and again ate alone in the dining room. On the way to his room the clerk reminded him in the form of a question, "Do you leave tomorrow?" So, it was time to think of his final plans for Atami and then to consider his return to Hokkaido. Tom slept again after lunch and awoke just in time for the evening meal.

He prepared for the last evening in Atami. There was a kind of restless anticipation because he planned to get drunk and then allow circumstances to carry him along. He dressed in fresh khakis he'd been saving, saw to it that his shoes and brass sparkled. He took two fresh packs of Camels and his cigarette lighter and all his Japanese currency folded thickly in a shirt pocket.

In the entertainment district in the early evening he strode into a small bar, greeted the hostesses with a double wave of both hands, slid into a booth, motioned to two hostesses to join him, lay the substantial pile of 100 yen notes on the table, unbuttoned his cuffs and rolled his sleeves above his wrists, loosened his tie and ordered sake.

The warm rice wine came in a small flask set in a bowl of hot water. Tom sipped off a half-dozen miniscule sake cupsful. Cigarettes were handed round and lighted. More flasks of the unpleasant wine were consumed and then according to a plan that accompanied the arrival of the mild intoxication Tom slid from the booth, pressed 100 yen notes into the protesting hostesses' hands, refused the offer of snacks hastily brought from the kitchen, and set off diagonally across the street to drink his way to the GI dance hall he'd visited the first night in Atami.

Tom strode affably into the next bar and drank

several flasks of sake. He became less interested in the responses of the bar personnel as he accepted their standardized courtesies.

He paid but flying visits to the next bars in the row along the street laughing out the word, sake, and waving money and making a joke out of shaking out fresh cigarettes to be lighted by the hostesses with three or four ashtrays before him each festooned with smoldering cigarettes and Tom insisting on his right as a customer to have each fresh cigarette lighted despite the concern of the hostesses for the others ranged in spokes around the ashtrays. He began to feel a heaviness in his head and tongue and his conversation and requests became minimal.

Emerging from a bar, his sake flask there only tasted, he stood in the street legs apart and head down breathing heavily and focused on the problem of making his way to the dance hall while any semblance of self-direction remained intact in his motor system.

He walked stiff-legged in the night air his head pushed forward looking past his eyebrows to find the way. He heard his breathing and he made humming and buzzing sounds in his throat. He rehearsed his behavior if anyone or anything crossed or annoyed him. He would throw bottles and ashtrays and would shove and push. He imagined and resolved insults and slights in rapid succession.

Rounding the corner of the dance hall building and taking the stairs by twos Tom thrust himself into the club and greeted all present, a good-sized crowd, with a mighty wave of his hand and then went to the bar to order beer. He was persuaded by a hostess to accompany her to a table. This give and take slowed somewhat more the momentum which had peaked and then slid over the height of enthusiasm which had built while climbing the stairs and now Tom sat chin on chest frowning and too dizzy to raise his head to drink from the glass of beer the initially puzzled but experienced hostess had poured. She lighted a cigarette and gave it to him.

It was now time to sweep the table clean with his arm in a mighty crash of wet glass, to bellow obscene challenges, to give and take dull blows, but the beer and cigarettes did their awful work and his plans were swept away on waves of vertigo and nausea that seized and shook him. He rose desperately to his feet and scurried bent over, head down, arms outstretched for the toilet. He swung around the toilet door and spewed against the tile wall a projectile of carelessly chewed roast beef, tomatoes and lettuce marinated in consommé, sake, gastric juices and half a glass of lager beer. His arms sought almost independently of his will to support his balance leaning against the wall but they collapsed and he stood with his head against the cool tiles of the wall his feet away from the hole in the floor toilet for just a moment before he spewed again and then a third time and a fourth time with successively severer stomach cramps.

And then there was only a thin sour sting of mucousy saliva roping from his lower lip and he suffered his system's retaliation upon itself. His stomach cramped and expelled nothing over and over and sweat broke out on his forehead and pricked his forearms and he wished he were unconscious.

After a time, his shirt wet with perspiration, he tried to leave the club unobtrusively, embarrassed and ashamed still totally drunk but not permitted the usual indifference and unawareness of a drunk. On his way out a Marine offered an insult, the stimulus for the brawl he'd anticipated and experienced in his imagination earlier in the evening, but he merely pushed the Marine out of the way and stumbled down the steps.

He was exhausted. He was ill. He was drunk, and after a short time he was lost. He climbed up hill streets that turned into steps, he trudged into dead-end alleys, he walked head down hazarding an occasional glance upward at his risk of aggravating the vertigo, scanning anxiously for landmarks but unwilling to subject his vertigo to the thorough punishment of a longer regard of the streets and vistas. Once he sat on a bench, forearms on knees, forehead on forearm and glimpsed the awfulness of his shoes and pant legs.

Finally, he let one street somewhat familiar in detail guide him to the strand. He stumbled with aching fatigue through the sand and shingle to the fish market. He followed the street that climbed the hill from there to the entertainment district, from there to the gate to the hotel grounds, to the hotel, to the stairs, to his cot in the foyer. He pulled off his shoes and pants and threw them into the bathtub. Further efforts impossible, he fell across the cot and slept.

Someone shook his shoulder and spoke to him. He looked up at a soldier. It was hot and stuffy and intensely bright in the foyer where he lay on the cot. He looked at the soldier. It was one of his roommates. Jesus Christ, they had awakened him earlier and gotten him on his feet and then had gone down to breakfast. They'd returned for their duffel bags. The train left in half an hour. There was a taxi waiting. They'd give him 10 minutes and if necessary, leave without hint.

Tom struggled into his wrinkled soiled clothing. He was still reeling from drunkedness or something even worse. He saw the room maids stripping the beds of linen, putting the sheets into wicker baskets. He stuffed the rest of his clothing and toilet gear into his duffel bag, cupped his hands at the sink and splashed water on his face and ran as best he could to the waiting taxi. In the cab the enormity of the hangover struck hard at his aching eyes and dry mouth. Sweat began to pour. Once he persuaded them to stop the cab but his efforts to vomit produced nothing and he was pulled back into the cab.

At the station he rummaged in his duffel bag for his travel papers, smoked a cigarette, and sat with his elbows on his knees, his eyes shut.

Once on the train he slumped against the window and slept until the train reached Tokyo. He was totally tired and incapable of caring for himself, so the two soldiers assumed his responsibilities. They led him to a place to sit and when some undetermined time later it was time to board the train they came and got him and took him to a seat and left him alone.

He rode for hours no longer sleepy but seeking sleep to avoid the discomfort and mess of himself. He went to the toilet and washed his face and combed his hair for the first time that day. His uniform was really a mess. It was rumpled and creased and had smudges and stains where he'd spilled things, or leaned, or sat, or sprawled on things. Tom went back to his seat and sat until dinner was announced and suddenly hungry was unable to eat anything at all.

The train and ferry trip back were spent in sleeping or in a state of reflection pondering his miserableness. Occasionally he was distracted from his hangover by some incident or scene witnessed from the train window. For a while he stood almost enjoying the nighttime fresh air in the rocking alcove between the sleeping cars. He was motioned back inside by the conductor.

By the time the train reached the ferry port of Aomori Tom still didn't feel good, but he didn't feel ill and his discomfort was more the consequences of his consciousness of his appearance than any remnant of the assault of alcohol and fatigue.

He ate some breakfast on the ferry boat taking small bites, chewing slowly and thoroughly. He left most of the food on the plate very conscious of the egg taste and the feel of the toast in his mouth. The dining room became stuffy and he sought relief outside in the fresh air.

He went through his duffel bag to appraise the least ravaged of his uniforms but even the least soiled clothing had been wadded up and stuffed into the bag and sat upon so Tom sought refuge in the less frequented areas of the ferry and avoided, he hoped, the eyes of his fellow passengers.

He arrived back at Camp Crawford while the Bandsmen were at dinner. He took his uniforms and underwear into the shower with him and soaped and scrubbed and rinsed them all. He did the same thing to them again in the laundry trough. He dressed in a cool clean set of fatigues.

In response to the queries of the Bandsmen wandering back to the barracks, Tom responded that the trip had been great.

Later after hanging up the clothing to dry he lay on his bunk smoking for the first time in a day-and-a-half and feeling really clean, cool and relaxed, comfortable. He was very glad to be back in camp and its routine.

CHAPTER 17

Tom had noticed full field packs and gear laid out and learned that the next morning they were scheduled for an exercise in preparation for amphibious training.

At one edge of the camp was an enormous open scaffolding with flights of steps leading up to a platform three stories high. The platform was surrounded by a solid railing. On the railing opposite the stairs was a rope net of the kind used in disembarking from troop ships into landing vessels.

There was a strong undercurrent of nervousness among the Bandsmen the next morning. Some handled their concern by morosely staring into space, others by elaborate teasing of others about their fears. Tom tended to rehearse over and over in his mind how he intended to accomplish the drill without injuring or embarrassing himself.

They formed up after breakfast. The Bandsmen remaining behind on housekeeping details offered their observations that the nets looked unsafe to them, cautioned them not to freeze on the net or fall from it. They marched in route step in two long lines on either side of the road conscious of the weight of their packs and gear, weapons and steel helmets.

Once at the training area a cadre sergeant explained they were to go over the railing five at a time. They were to dress on the climber to the right during their descent. They were to hook their elbows into the net if they felt panicky.

They were to avoid treading on the men below them. They had only so much time as a unit to accomplish the task and would have to repeat the exercise as a unit if necessary until it was completed in the time limit.

Tom was mid-way in the long line threading its way up the stairs. It was startling how high only one or two landings brought him. He could look across the tops of the barracks' roofs and the scattered trees. He felt pressure in his abdomen and wanted to urinate. He decided he wouldn't look down anymore and would concentrate on excluding all stimuli outside his immediate reach.

Up on the platform and waiting his turn to go over and down the net there was a delay occasioned by a Bandsman on the net complaining of vertigo and above and below there was some coming and going as two cadre went down the net to talk the frightened Bandsman down.

At last Tom's rank's turn came. His whole body was tense. He moved very deliberately on the net. There was the shock as a blow struck the side of his face. He felt pain, fear, and then anger after realizing the climber above and to the left had accidentally swung a boot into his face.

It was hard climbing down. The weight was all on his arms and shoulders. His feet went in and under and provided no support. He heard himself grunting with effort and concern. The men on the right were cursing the net, their gear, the experience. The net would sway, it would tense and slacken, suddenly someone above yelled to duck and Tom felt a hard object glance heavily off his pack and heard it clatter off other gear below. Someone had lost his steel helmet and it had fallen on the climbers. There were curses, indignant shouts and from those below watching there was laughter.

It didn't take long to climb down. Tom slipped to one knee next to a Bandsman who was straining to hold the bottom of the net secure against the pull of the swaying, clambering bodies above.

He joined the ranks of Bandsmen who had preceded him in the net and was allowed to loosen his gear, sit, and smoke a cigarette. A small group was trying to persuade the man who earlier had shown fear by freezing on the net and calling for help that it was no big deal, but he was angry with embarrassment so after a while he was left alone with his shame.

Tom had many invitations as the weeks went on to double date as some of the men and boys settled into semi- or quite-permanent relationships in town with Japanese girls. These girls almost always it seemed had girlfriends or relatives who would also like to establish one of these usually advantageous liaisons. The structure of the thing depended on the degree of the domestication of the soldier. Some really enjoyed playing house, and they would set-up housekeeping, eat meals the girl prepared, sleep on stolen GI sheets and blankets, wash with stolen GI soap, and purchase quantities of appliances for the girl and his in-laws. The soldiers often turned the greater portion of their pay over to the girls who would budget for rent, food, beer, and entertainment. These soldiers were homebodies who enjoyed nothing more than bringing a guest home to show off the little woman who busied around preparing snacks and beverages while the little men of the house bathed, changed into kimonos and then spent the evening in conversation. To many young men the role of husband and the accessibility of sex on whim was quite irresistible.

Once, while visiting a Bandsman at his home, he met the girl's best friend, a woman in her late twenties with thick glasses and almost matronly mannerisms. She was pleasant and obliging but, in his opinion, quite plain. They ate, went to a movie, and in an aside his friend mentioned, almost as a duty to do so, that the woman seemed very favorably impressed with Tom and did he like her. There might be something there for Tom if he played his cards right.

Tom really did feel like going back to the post after the movie but the woman gave several girlish tugs at his arm so he assented and joined them for a night cap.

Back in the room his host and hostess began petting heavily to his slight embarrassment. The woman asked Tom if he liked her and he said, "Yes." In an instant bedding was unfolded and the girls conferred in a business like way about how affairs should be arranged. The light was put out and Tom and the woman embraced. She put aside her glasses and assisted him in undressing. He joined her under the coverlets. Her body was smooth and cool. She kissed him aggressively and ran her hands over his body. They had intercourse and then she rubbed and soothed and massaged Tom's back, arms and legs until he fell asleep.

In the cold grey of the early morning she awakened him, helped him to dress, and they walked hand-in-hand to the bus stop and waited for the bus to arrive. She looked at him and told him she wanted to see him again that night. Tom said, "Yes," but he wasn't sure. His friend told him during the bus ride back to camp that there was another room available in the building, that Tom should settle down. Fumiko was a great girl, that Tom would avoid the risk of VD, any number of arguments. But Tom didn't want to go with the same girl all the time and playhouse. He didn't want to be responsible or answerable to any one for any reason. He didn't want to travel the same little circuit of the mock domestic treadmill.

Tom did go back that evening and the woman was very warm and affectionate. He wished she were prettier, but she was nice and relaxed, and Tom would have enjoyed himself if he could have been less concerned about appearing to commit himself to something. The three of them treated Tom as family. They made plans for him in his role of half a couple. They would visit a mountain spa next weekend. Under the covers that night the woman did appropriate and exquisite things. Sated, Tom was kneaded to sleep again.

The woman held both arms around him as they walked to the bus stop the next morning. She told him she liked him very much. He was to come back and they would stay together in their own place.

Back at camp Tom resolved to have no more to do with the three. He told his friend who became angry and implied he would be the cause of some crisis involving him own arrangement. Tom resisted the cajoling, queries, the disgusted surrender of the friendship, assertions he was letting a buddy down, that he was unreasonably deficient in his answers why he wouldn't even try the relationship for a week. Didn't Tom like the girl? Didn't Tom enjoy doing things as a foursome? Wasn't the girl nice, and so on?

Tom spent the next several evenings on the post and then at the EM Club in Sapporo he saw the woman standing in the foyer outside the dining room just as he had seen Toshiko some weeks before. He turned away and when he had finished his meal she was gone also.

One morning, in formation, it was announced that the Bandsmen were to have their individual aptitudes for the acquisition of Morse code skills tested. This was part of a sweep through the Division to uncover talents that could be exploited in filling gaps in the Army's communication needs at the time. So, the Bandsmen were marched to a nearby barracks that was set up with tables and chairs. At one end was some electronic gear that included a record player and there was a NCO to read the test instructions and give the test.

The usual identification was filled in at the heading of the test form and a brief introduction to the test was read. A steel needle was lowered onto the 78 record, a rich fruity voice boomed out of the three inch speaker with a tone of even tempered indifference that was to prove maddening within a short time. The voice explained that certain combinations of short and long tones would represent letters of the alphabet. The tones would be repeated in a moment without his explanation and they were to mark the letters they represented in the spaces provided on the answer sheet.

Tom resolved to try to do well. The instruction came rapidly but still deliberately with no hint of urgency in the narrator's voice or that the task would be, within moments of the start, impossible. Scarcely a quarter of the way through the test Tom snorted in frustration, lay his pencil down and glanced around the room at the others. A few were busily making marks on their papers seemingly in response to the blurred syncopation of the tones. Most were looking restlessly around or out the window. Now the record produced buzzes and clicks in addition to the tones.

The NCO insisted they sit through the second side of the record. By that time everyone was disgusted by the experience. When they filed out they were more angry than anything else. None of the Bandsmen qualified for further training, as a consequence of the testing performance.

About a month after Tom's return from the R&R to Atami the Bandsmen were all delighted to learn a junket had been arranged for them. There was to be a journey to Tokyo to perform at the Ernie Pyle Theater, a performing facility in Tokyo of immense proportions where the tradition was that no armed forces personnel performed in uniform. They were provided with attire from the theater's stock of costumes in its own wardrobe.

It was a huge undertaking for the company clerk to cut the quantity of orders and vouchers needed to transport, lodge, and feed the 75 Bandsmen and officers on the journey to and return from Tokyo.

The Bandsmen spent their time before the departure in rehearsal and in fine-tuning the gleaming polish of their brass and leather and the crisp creases of their khakis carefully folded and then placed in their duffel bags.

This time the entire Band Company retraced Tom's trip on the train and ferry south down the long island of Honshu from the northern landscape to the lush vegetation of the main island, past Sendai the headquarters of the 40th Division, to Tokyo, and then transport by olive-drab school busses to the Meiji Hotel and its splendid dining room where the Bandsmen were dined, if not wined, with elegantly complete meals.

The junket was filled with full schedules of organized sightseeing. They were taken to the Meiji Museum where the process of the industrialization was traced, if not the westernization of Japan. They saw the Imperial moat and Imperial roof tiles. They went to the Tokyo EM Club and ate steak and sat in club chairs before club coffee tables and had their picture taken by club photographers, all this their first full day in Tokyo.

The next morning after breakfast served at tables for four with linen, full silver and china settings, they were bussed to the theater where they were fitted into their performing garb. This turned out to be vaguely Latin

American in effect consisting of black trousers, white rayon shirts with wide collars open at the neck, full sleeves with tight cuffs and red cummerbund-like sashes. The dressers, Japanese women, measured and fitted them with quick efficiency. And then the Bandsmen were given a couple of hours to wander in the immediate neighborhood of the theater in downtown Tokyo before the matinee.

The Bandsmen all returned as scheduled, were powdered, lipsticked, and rouged. They combed their hair carefully and performed for the afternoon audience of armed forces personnel and their families, some American civilian employees. The first half featured the symphonic band in a couple of suites and concert marches. After a brief intermission they presented their works for male chorus, the combo novelty acts; jazz, Dixie, country, the stand-up comic as MC. It was a fast paced professional show that lasted a bit over an hour and was well received and generously applauded. The Bandsmen then hung around the theater lounging in the seats and ate a box supper before the early evening performance which again went well.

They returned to the hotel that night, departed Tokyo the next morning and were back at Camp Crawford late the night of the sixth day and on the seventh they rested.

A sizeable portion of the Band was rounded up one Saturday afternoon from the barracks, the PX, the EM and NonCom Clubs and hurried into khakis with the intelligence only that they were to make an appearance of some sort in Sapporo later on in the afternoon. They got dressed, each with his particular response to the unexpected. Grumbling, laughter, acceptance, indifference. A couple of Bandsmen copied rapidly from the director's score the parts for the different instruments of the Kimigaiyo, the Japanese nation anthem.

Open trucks took the Bandsmen, their instruments, music stands, and folding chairs to a small green park at the foot of one of the major commercial avenues in downtown Sapporo. They set up just below a raised platform festooned with banners and lanterns.

On the platform were a number of Japanese dignitaries in dark suits. Most were elderly men white-haired, and an oddity, an American civilian in a dark suit accompanied by his wife wearing a pastel rose suit and an enormous white straw hat. The two Americans had such a soft vulnerable look compared to the uniformed American men and women Tom had become accustomed to.

The band played several concert marches from their music folders and then sat through some short speeches in Japanese and it was not until the remarks of the American that Tom knew he was participating in a ceremony that marked the signing of the peace treaty, the beginning of a new relationship between Japan and the United States. It was the end of the conquered/victor relationship. It created a strange inner sensation in Tom. As a soldier of the occupation he had felt something of the policeman or institutional guard representing the interests of the United States and now the conquered were no longer delinquents but could assert, if necessary, their equality. A lot of the behavior of the soldiers justified, if at all by the previous relationship, would no longer be appropriate.

The speakers finished in short order to applause, but not to tumultuous applause. The Japanese nation anthem, the Kimigaiyo, was performed and then a gesture not patronizing and probably meant graciously. A three-wheeled delivery vehicle appeared next to the Army trucks as they were loading and several cases of quarts of Japanese beer were set down by the gate of one of the trucks. There was some conversation back and forth until it was understood that this was a donation by the Japanese businessmen to express their appreciation for the band's participation. All of a sudden, the role of the soldiers as conquerors was over and they were in the position of accepting several cases of warm Japanese beer from the well-to-do members of the community to whom the bandsmen were outside participants in the achievement of their majority.

The cases of beer were lifted onto the truck and carried back to the post. Tom didn't see the beer after that. He didn't know who took it and drank it.

By now the short summer was over. The Division had arrived in Japan at the end of winter. Tom had experienced spring and the rainy, hot summer, and now the leaves of the forests were turning color. There was bite to the air except in the full sun at mid-day.

For purposes of morale and to celebrate the reconsolidation of the band, the division was returning all its units to Camp Crawford and more substantial winter quarters from the tent communities in the field. Arrangements were made for a band picnic at Lake Shikotsu, a scenic destination in a Japanese national park.

As many bandsmen as possible were relieved from the usual housekeeping work details. Genuine sympathy was felt for those left behind. The party consisted of two trucks packed with soldiers, a weapon's carrier with supplies for the picnic, and the CO's jeep.

The arrival point was on the shore of the lake, a shingle beach under the trees at the end of a ragged line of refreshment and concession stands.

The soldiers under the relaxation of all discipline changed into bathing trunks or stripped to underwear and tested the water, but to their dismay it was like ice. There were no more voluntary immersions. Cases of beer were iced down in galvanized washtubs. Someone started an unnecessarily large bonfire for roasting wieners, and tins and mess trays of food were set out on sawhorse supported tables.

Some of the bandsmen went to the Japanese refreshment stands to purchase large bottles of sake, snacks, and souvenirs. Another group went to negotiate with motor launch operators for excursions on the water. The lake in response to the winds of an approaching storm front had begun to kick up slight white caps. The day which had dawned clear became overcast and the chill wind caused most of the bandsmen to dress again.

Tom had walked a mile on either side of the picnic

site and had found little of interest, so he'd returned to lounge against a tree trunk and drink beer, enough beer now to be quietly drunk.

At one point, Tom was aware that the wind had risen to storm proportions and that many things were happening that fortunately did not involve him personally. Tom knew for instance that one boat excursion had been assayed, that the boat, a rather large one, had experienced difficulty, and had taken on so much water that it sank next to the pier while the Bandsmen were scrambling out of the wildly tossing craft.

Tom also witnessed an incident in which a giant of a Bandsman had first good-naturedly, and then in an unanticipated burst of rage, picked up at least four men in turn and threw them over his head into the lake, or at least at the lake. Only one of them, perhaps the most fortunate, landed in the water. The other three landed on the rocks at the water's edge.

The surf and waves occasioned by the wind washed up and partially extinguished the bonfire. It swept away one sawhorse, assorted packages and items of company issue as well as personal items, boots and socks, cameras and fatigue caps.

Tom watched as one corner of a refreshment stand was attacked or run into by soldiers and it collapsed with some damage to an overhang, some chairs, and a bench.

He drank on, occasionally eating a cold wiener. There were sufficient Bandsmen sober because of their disinterest in alcohol to reload the trucks, police the litter, persuade, bully, or direct the drinkers onto the trucks. Tom was assisted into a truck, felt incapable of sitting up, and slept not really uncomfortably on the floor of the truck all the way back to camp.

One night, Tom walked into a small bar in Sapporo where an acquaintance of his from division headquarters was sitting in a booth with two hostesses. Tom was waved over and invited to listen to what one of the hostesses had said. She was asked to repeat her comments. It was that the 45th was going to Korea before Christmas. Well, that was two months away. Where had she heard that? Tom disbelieved the rumor himself. Why would a National Guard division be committed to combat? That question would be answered later, of course, when he witnessed the extent of the disintegration and chaos of the 1st Cav, the division that they would replace.

The hostess's assertion had an odd effect on Tom. He felt as if he were listening to a spy or an enemy agent, one of the enemy so frequently referred to in the dreary continuing Saturday morning TI&E lectures. But the girl was so matter-of-fact and self-assured. She said she would be sorry to see them go because the 45th GIs had been good GIs. They had been generous and for the most part courteous and that the Japanese girls of her acquaintance didn't look forward to the return of the 1st Cav to Hokkaido. The conversation turned to other things and Tom didn't bother repeating the rumor to his friends when he got back to camp.

CHAPTER 18

With the onset of winter, the Bandsmen were to move to quonset huts on the other side of the post. The old brick barracks were scrubbed, GI'ed, and left behind for the novelty of the quonsets, metal half-circles on concrete pads.

The band occupied two-and-a-half quonsets on a Company street. Tom was assigned to the group of 15 who would share half of the third quonset with an exotic set of Asians and Asian- Americans, regular Army members of a CIC unit. They weren't members of the 45th. They merely slept in quarters provided by the division, ate occasionally on the post and came and went, usually went, for a week or two and then returned to spend most of several days dozing on their cots before leaving again.

Tom never got to know any of them very well. Most were older men who didn't seem particularly friendly even with members of their own group. He wasn't sure all of them knew English.

They were all remarkably physically fit. It was Tom's impression that they went underground, and their job was to discover black market and currency irregularities. They did wear civilian clothing as often as not when they left, nondescript black or blue laborers' clothing for the most part. While relaxing in the quonset most of them wore a kimono as did many of the Bandsmen by this time.

Once one of the older CIC operatives, an Okinawan whom the Bandsmen called or at least referred to as Chief, came back from some drinking experience, his khakis still crisp and immaculate, and with a fierceness Tom had never witnessed under any circumstances, smashed in the door and sides of a metal wall locker with chopping blows of his right hand.

The snow came shortly after the move into the quonsets and in a week it was waist high in the open areas between the barracks and the drill fields and lay in immense drifts beside the buildings. There were long hours with nothing to do really. Outdoor training for the Bandsmen was impractical. Shoveling paths in the snow became another housekeeping chore, only the principal streets were plowed free.

It was during this week of heavy snow they learned that the Division was in fact ordered to exchange places with the 1st Cavalry Division in Korea. The 45th would take over the Cav's sector in the west central front facing the Chinese. The Cav would return to Hokkaido for reorganization, retraining, and reequipment. The CO announced this as the Bandsmen sat crowded on bunks and footlockers in one of the quonsets.

The response to the news was silence. An advance guard would leave Japan in a week. A clerk from the Band would be going to the replacement depot at Yongdongpo located between Inchon and Seoul to take care of the Band's paperwork. A member of the 1st Cav Band would be expected from Korea in about a week's time to do whatever was necessary to prepare for the arrival of his unit in Japan.

The later reaction of the Bandsmen was extreme but quiet. Tom was unable to tell anyone that he was enormously excited and jubilant over the opportunity to experience Korea. After the initial novelty of Japan, Tom felt he was on the periphery of the real military experience and longed for closer contact with the war. Tom shrank from being categorized as gung ho. The draftees' disdain for the regular who sought out getting his ass shot off was too much in the atmosphere around him, but Tom felt Korea would represent the logical consequence of all the training in infantry tactics and weaponry he'd received.

It was Camp Polk all over again. Some Bandsmen sat quietly in despair, morose or grumpy. Others began to bustle around making arrangements to have created and mailed home the clutter in the form of radios, cameras, and other impediments they'd accumulated from the PX and in town.

They were issued winter caps with fuzzy ear flaps, shoe packs with felt innersoles, and they were instructed on the number of pairs of socks to be worn with them. They were issued huge OD overcoats reaching to their ankles with zip out blanket linings, mittens and mitten liners, long underwear, and as many as would go around, down sleeping bags. Tom didn't get one of these and was to experience some discomfort and sleepless hours later on because of the cold.

There was an intense interest in going to town and most of the Bandsmen went off post every opportunity given to them, even the letter writers went.

Tom went one weekend with an acquaintance who had a girlfriend in Otaru, the off-limits port town that had been Tom's first sight of Japan.

They took a small electrified train to Otaru, his friend laden with gifts from the PX, cigarettes, an electric iron, cosmetics. The girlfriend was a woman in her late 20's who managed her family-owned bar in a quiet neighborhood of Otaru. His friend had gone there for several months and was a friend of the whole family.

They reached the utter greyness and soot, and grey stucco, and wet wood, and damp streets of Qtaru after a journey through the snowy landscape of Hokkaido. Farmhouses buried in snow, flat rectangles of snow above the rice paddies.

They walked all bundled up in their winter gear to the bar where they went through the bar to the living quarters behind and Tom was introduced to the girlfriend and her smiling elderly father and less smiling elderly mother.

A neighborhood child was sent running to fetch a female companion for Tom and in a bit a very interesting somewhat aloof young woman appeared in a cloth coat with a fur collar. Her face was more sculptured and thinner than those of the usually plump round-faced farm girls who worked the soldier bars.

They decided to go to the movies and as the town was off limits they were objects of interest to the Japanese on the street who saw few Americans on foot in the town.

The movie house was not heated so they sat close to

one another and watched a samurai epic replete with gutteral ejaculations and scorned women, horses rattling along, sword play, the stylized low catter-wauling of the aroused cinematic samurai. Everyone in the theater smoked and ate sweets. Tom and his group watched the movie until his friend's girlfriend decided it was time to go.

They walked the streets of the town until they reached a park overlooking the harbor where children were skiing down the snow covered steps that led up to some monument of religious significance. The children couldn't have been older than seven or eight, but they managed their ski run with skill and elan. Tom didn't see one child fall.

He was told that after the heavier snows the children skied to school and the workers of the town skied to their jobs in the interval before the streets were cleared.

Tom's friend brought out a camera from between the layers of his clothing and Tom took a picture of the soldier and the two women standing in the high hilltop park with the harbor behind and below them, his friend moulding a snowball. Then Tom took a picture or two of the cheerful children, skis strapped to their backs, who were climbing the stair step ski run.

They went back to the girlfriend's bar and sat and drank beer and ate rice crackers. The girl's mother had gone somewhere further back into the living quarters, but the elderly father sat and smiled and offered comments which his daughter would occasionally translate into English.

They drank some soup and ate from a bowl of tiny

octopus. They listened to American popular songs on a portable record player purchased at the PX, one of a number of appliances, radios, and so on that had been joined by the electric iron. The old man accepted the cartons of cigarettes with thanks, bobbing his head.

Later when his friend's girlfriend went to prepare the sleeping mats Tom was surprised that he and his own female friend were to share the same room, in fact, the same enormous pile of comforters that half-filled the tiny frigid unheated room.

Tom and the other soldier went to the toilet and then back in the bedroom undressed but for their underwear and burrowed under the covers.

The two women appeared a bit later dressed in kimono. The light was extinguished, and the Bandsmen were embraced. Tom was taken aback that he was embraced by his friend's girlfriend, but somehow that was the plan and as the bed warmed up, he felt the situation less strange and less awkward. He was not interested in the activities of the other couple and had his own very good time.

In the night Tom was awakened with the sharp need to urinate and almost froze in his quest for the toilet, the slate floor was searing cold against his bare feet. When Tom returned to the coverlets the women exchanged partners and he sleepily responded to the stimulation of the woman with whom he's spent the afternoon. Afterwards he smoked a cigarette and went back to sleep.

Tom was awakened early by the women who had

already dressed. They had their coats on in the cold room. Tom dressed and went with the others out into the street. It was a cold, raw, over-cast morning. On their walk to the train station they were stopped by a young man who spoke to the women and gestured toward a crowd gathered at the steps of some public building two blocks ahead.

The women pulled on the soldiers' arms and they walked a street parallel to the one on which the activity was under way. The women said a crowd was being harangued by communists who were urging them to protest against the presence of the American Army in Japan.

Tom was interested in that, half-curious to know what level of provocation would be produced by his walking through that crowd in a U.S. uniform. Half, or more really than half, relieved that such an encounter had been avoided by the warning and detour, he continued to the train station.

The women waited with them until the electric train came. They all stood close together on the platform. Then it was time to leave and Tom thanked the women. The one woman put a small package wrapped with decorated paper in his pocket and hurried away. She turned back in the street and waved goodbye while the train moved away.

Back at camp the Bandsmen learned they were all now restricted to the post and they would be leaving Japan on very short notice. Tom's CO told him that because he was 17 he could request a transfer from the 45th that would be entering the zone of combat. Tom declined the opportunity. Others didn't. Some were to remain in Japan for medical reasons. One sergeant was engaged in a monumental effort to obtain permission to marry a woman who had been a registered prostitute. In addition, the woman had shadows of TB in her lungs that would prevent her from accompanying him to the U.S. But he persisted and in some convolution of procedures and appeals he was transferred to another unit assigned to remain in Japan.

The advance guard, a party of one, a supply clerk from the 1st Cav Band, arrived at Camp Crawford. He was a tall, thin, likable older man in his late 20's who politely listened and agreed to each and every proposal made for his comfort and convenience. He went quietly to the PX and drank and ate. He accepted invitations to play pool at the Sergeants club, but when not actively engaged at the initiation of someone he sat on the edge of his bunk and looked thoughtfully down at the floor.

Hello, memory. Let's dig up a bit more or else. I'm afraid you'll have to assay a bit more to accomplish the objectives listed on page one. But the epic of Korea still hasn't been filmed, or written, or serialized on the PBS, all Alex Rooted or Evelyn Waughed.

The snows and storms continued, and the Bandsmen took snapshots of each other waist deep in the snow outside the quonset huts. They spent hours smoking and sleeping as all training and activities ceased as they waited in the huts for their orders to leave.

Their duffel bags were packed with the summer issue of clothing, the field packs and cargo packs were crammed with field issue. More sleeping bags were issued and then withdrawn. No parkas were issued although the CO turned up in one. The men still wore the bulky overcoats with the wool blanket-like linings. They were issued somewhat different shoe packs with the same felt inner soles but with more complex instructions on the kinds of socks to be worn and now each man had five pairs of shoes, two low cuts, two boots, and the shoe packs that resembled enormous galoshes.

Then one morning around 10:00 one of the sergeants stated simply that they'd be leaving that day. They were told to roll their blankets into their shelter halves which were then strapped into an inverted U around the top and sides of the field pack. They were to turn in their sheets and pillows. Immediately a rustle of concern. They were restricted to the barracks and some smokers were low on cigarettes. After some negotiation two men were permitted to go to the PX with orders for cartons of cigarettes, lighter fluid, and matches.

Everything was packed. The men and boys lay on the bare mattresses of their bunks. Their packs and duffel bags lay in the aisles. There they waited until 11:00 that night when they were told they'd be leaving in 15 minutes. The men struggled into field jackets and overcoats. They were weighted down with their bags containing their full summer issue of khakis; two shirts, two trousers, and the woolen issues of two shirts, two trousers, Eisenhower jacket, field caps, dress cap, two sets of fatigues, field pants, shelter half, entrenching tool, canteen, first-aid packet, weapon and bayonet, blankets, helmet, mess gear, socks, underwear, and much personal gear, licit and illegal, mostly Japanese liquor. And some managed even more, a radio, a typewriter, and Alden Ring had his cello.

The men and boys struggled through the doorway and out into the darkness of the company street. Some held their duffel bags across the front of their bodies, an awkward dead weight. Others dragged them in the snow. They stood in ranks and then were marched toward the railhead some two miles distant. Where are the trucks? No trucks. They were stumbling in the dark across the frozen rutted snow. The men were soon sweating mightily. Someone up ahead had a flashlight. All else was pitch black. Some men had persuaded a companion to lift and balance the duffel bag across their shoulders atop the pack. The bags pushed their helmets forward over their eyes. The bags became unbalanced, they fell. The pack straps cut off the circulation to the arms.

They pulled into the arm pits and pinched and bruised. Men slipped and fell against one another. There was no laughter or cursing, just the sounds of strenuous effort and the release of pent-up breaths.

There were delays and the men stood trying to shift or manage their burdens somehow. Finally, during one pause Tom left the formation and stumbled into a shallow ditch and just lay on his back in the snow on top of his pack and then scrambled to his feet when he heard the column move forward again. At the rail head the men removed their gear and handed it up through the narrow doors of the Japanese railway carriages.

The men sat in the dark cars perspiring, silent, exhausted. The Japanese railway men waved lanterns. Someone said it was after 1:00 in the morning. Tom dozed as the train started, stopped, started until they were at the docks at Otaru.

Again, there was only the illumination of the train crew lanterns, a few scattered yellowish-lights around the warehouses. They dragged their gear out of the train and helped each other with packs and duffel bags and weapons.

There was a formation and roll call. Numbers were chalked on their helmets and again they stumbled in the dark over railroad tracks, around warehouses, up and down ramps to the pier where a dark transport loomed over them. They struggled up the too narrow gangplank through a blackout curtain into the interior of the ship.

There were Navy enlisted men lined up watching them curiously, offering help if one of the soldiers dropped something or attempted to adjust his burden. They made their way down step steel stairs to an open bay with ranks of bunks in tiers and were told to count themselves off and to take their bunks.

The air in the bay was fresh and warm, the bunks were made up with soft blue blankets, crisp sheets, pillows with pillowcases. The steel floors and walls were clean and cool. A sailor appeared at the hatch way at the head of the stairs and said there was hot coffee and cocoa for any who wished it in the crews' mess.

The soldiers for the most part simply lay or sat and wondered what kind of ship they'd encountered. They learned it was a Navy attack transport. Clean, well run, and the sailors treated them deferentially and courteously as if they were clients or guests.

CHAPTER 19

The next morning the soldiers ate in a large low-ceilinged galley seated at tables with the ship's crew. They chose their food, as much as they wished, from steam tables, cafeteria style. They drank coffee brewed in enormous steel vats, the grounds tied in five pound sugar sacks. They were permitted to sit at the tables and linger over the coffee smoking cigarettes.

They went on deck and discovered the ship was not as large as they'd assumed from their experience coming to Japan. There were only a few hundred troops on board. The lean ship raced through the deep blue waters, the wake of icy blue, the bow wave whiter than the snow on the mountains on their port. They raced past small fishing boats, through acres of jelly fish. They noticed a destroyer pacing them to starboard.

The men and boys found places on the deck sheltered from the wind but in the sun and smoked and talked about the good chow. The sailors who didn't seem to have much to do would come and listen politely to the soldiers' comments and would answer questions about the size and speed of the transport and the armaments at the battle stations.

And so that day passed and that night in their bunks those soldiers awake for one reason or another noticed the tempo of the ship's engines slowed and there was a bit more rolling than pitching. Those who awakened during the night would go to the head and find men sitting quietly smoking. They were the ones whose imaginations or homesickness didn't permit them an easy sleep.

Tom was awakened in the morning and noticed they were hurried through their breakfast. The sailors this morning seemed to have duties after all and there was no lingering over cigarettes. They were told to get their gear together and to wait below.

The vibrations and sounds seemed to indicate the ship was moving very slowly if at all. They sat below in their overcoats, leaning against their packs and duffel bags. Those who could slept.

Time for the noon meal came and went. The ship moved forward, they heard the splash of the bow wave against the bulkhead. The ship paused, there was the rattle of chains and the whine of electric engines. They were told to rise and climb up the steel steps. It was still an effort to stand and an agony to climb. The carefully arranged straps and harnesses cut into their arms or pulled sideways.

But they made it up stepping high over and through the bulkhead doors, past the sailors who urged them on and out into the bright winter light where they learned to their horror they were to go over the side and down landing nets into a large landing vessel that lay, thankfully, quietly alongside some 15 or 20 feet below the deck of the transport. Sailors hurriedly pushed and lifted them as they climbed over the steel rail to the net. Then they held them there as they attempted to secure handholds in the thick cable of the rope net.

When Tom was secured to the net his duffel bag was placed on the top of his pack and he climbed down seeking with first one foot and then the other a foothold. He was reluctant to trust his weight to but one hand at a time and slid his hands down releasing his grip but enough for his weight to pull him down.

But the distance was short and soon he was on a ramp and being urged down some steel steps to the bottom of the open landing craft and was being moved by shoves from the crew to make room for the next arrivals. He was standing with the others shoulder to shoulder and face to back shifting his balance slightly as the craft rose and fell with an occasional swell. Tom noticed all the sailors were wearing life vests.

The craft was filled, there were orders to cast off, a tremendous roar of the landing craft's engines and they moved forward, the wind biting cold. The superstructure of the transport disappeared.

The trip took about 15 minutes. There was a decrease in the engine speed, and idling, and a jolting stop. The front wall of the craft rattled down onto a steel mesh roadway laid over a shingle beach below a concrete sea wall. This landing craft was a large open metal box. One end of the box fell down and revealed a shingle beach. The oily gasoline smell of the landing craft was pushed aside by the sharp sea-weedy smell of the beach.

The men and boys trooped up the ramp, across the

steel mesh, up the steps of the sea wall, rusty iron reinforcement jutting and twisting out of the crumbling concrete. Much green slime and seaweed. Up to a line of waiting open trucks and in the street dusty snow, the cold piercing now, the smell of burnt coal and wood and charcoal, of dung and feces.

Here were unpainted wooden buildings, beaten earth streets and alleys, piles of rubble, adults in padded clothing pushing rusty bicycles, the harsh features of the Koreans, their rubber shoes with turned up Ali Baba toes.

Into the trucks. It was late afternoon now, overcast and were other scaffold like tables outside in a rectangular area surrounded by a wire fence more than ten feet high. As it was dark and unheated in the tent anyway Tom went outside to eat and saw this: Maybe 20 soldiers standing eating. Dusk, almost dark. At the fence 40 or more women and children reaching through with their hands palms up. The Koreans were silent until the soldiers went to the garbage cans to scrape the remains of their meal from the mess kits into the cans. Then the women and children pleaded for the leftovers. The Koreans pushed and crowded violently along the fence.

Tom was then unable to eat but he was unable to submit to the hands grasping for food. He emptied his mess kit into the half-filled garbage can and went back to his tent.

At breakfast he watched, as he ate, the Korean guards beat back a crowd when a gate was opened for the holders of the garbage concession who came to empty the garbage cans into their truck.

There were further flurries of paperwork, forms to complete. Blankets and woolen sleeping bags were turned in. Tom was on fire watch and missed this issue of used down-filled sleeping bags. They were patched, stained with some kind of indelible soil, and the feathers stuck through the material. Tom awakened the next morning to the ludicrous sight of his tentmates with tiny, downy feathers in their hair.

This was fire watch. It was best to pull this duty during the day. If not, one would be awakened, say at 3:00 in the morning in a bitterly cold tent to dress by flashlight. Shaking with cold he would stumble out into the dark. The cold made it painful to breathe. The soldier who had summoned Tom told him to watch this and spit and shined his flashlight on the phlegm frozen on the ground. He said the same thing happens when you piss. It freezes on the ground.

Tom became alert as he walked the perimeter of the tents. He was amazed by the intensity of the cold. For the first time in his life he experienced cold that was potentially life threatening, as much so as a poisonous snake or a fall from a height. Tom would have to be careful or he could actually freeze.

Some of the men lay awake in the tents, the sleepers slept. Some soldiers stopped by on their way back to their tents with tales of prostitutes outside the fence and the kinds of sex that could be had with a wire fence between the participants, pretty much variations on hand jobs and blow jobs.

Also, eggs could be obtained for cigarettes or dollars and you could get Korean liquor. Tom didn't go to the fence, but he did ask someone who did go to buy eggs for him and he fried them in his mess kit on the tent stove. He fried them in margarine saved from the mess tent. The eggs stuck in the margarine as they cooked so he scrambled them with his fork and ate a half dozen hot and delicious.

The men and boys were given an opportunity to exchange military script for won and to take a truck into Seoul. Tom marveled at the insubstantiality of the thousands of won he received in exchange for $10. He took his place in the back of the truck. They drove past bombed out industrial areas into the city.

In Seoul Tom and two companions walked in the middle of the streets.

There were winter vegetables for sale. He saw no shops with consumer goods. Most of the Koreans averted their eyes. An occasional tough would solicit them for prostitutes but only one persisted at all before he cursed them and left them alone.

Up ahead in the street was a group of five children laughing about something. Then the children spied the soldiers and rushed toward them whining and keening. One child in particular aroused horror. He was clad in a fatigue shirt only, bare footed and head shaved. His head showed appalling open sores. His legs were black with filth, his hands like filthy claws. Perhaps he was eight years old. Tom shook his arm loose from the grasp of this child. The children followed them for a block or two. Tom was offended by the children's laughter before their cries of distress.

It was a lesson Tom puzzled out later after telling of the experience many times and listening to different responses to the anecdote. We are incapable of intense preoccupation with one emotion. Even in extreme physical distress it is possible to laugh if the situation continues. Tom saw photos of these same children, spectacular in their distresses, in some magazine later on, LIFE or TIME probably. A photograph captured the children's clawed hands, their shaven heads, their pleading ever and anon. And Tom had seen them barefoot and shivering, laughing and joking on a street corner in Seoul.

As the soldiers made their way back to the truck rendezvous by some military club or PX through streets dressed in banners decorated with Korean script they were stopped by a Turkish soldier in a filthy parka and woolen cap who made sweeping gestures first pantomiming drink and then questioning movements. As they had no idea where anything to drink could be found they shook their heads and shrugged their shoulders. The Turk laughed and slapped them on the back and shouted, "OK, OK."

The talk was when Tom got back to his tent that Kenny, a drummer, had been arrested and taken away on drug dealing charges; cocaine, heroin, pills, and powders. Four or five CIC agents had come to the tent, opened

Kenny's duffel bag, and took things out of it. Then they took Kenny away. Apparently, Kenny was a dealer. Tom hadn't known that. He knew that some Bandsmen used drugs but it wasn't a blatant thing. It was handled very circumspectly. No one from the Band saw Kenny again.

A few more of the soldiers of the band were issued parkas. The supply sergeant said he was trading with other outfits. He traded a generator for 20 parkas, and he had a lead on some more.

They were told they were to join their division north of Seoul on the MLR as the rotation of the 1st Cav was now almost complete. They were issued clips of ammunition for their carbines for the first time. Some ammo was rustled up for Tom's M1. They were told that from now on they were to have full clips of ammunition in their weapons.

There was also a market in .45 automatics which changed hands for about $100. Tom had exchanged his carbine for a spare M1 because he admired the size and heft of the rifle. It was the basic weapon of the infantryman and therefore good enough for him.

The men and boys climbed into the tarpaulin covered trucks one morning for their ride north. They sat facing each other with their weapons between their knees. Soon the yellow powder of the road blew back into the trucks and covered their faces and clothing.

They drove north over rough roads through villages with the Asian smells, trucks crowding the pedestrians off the road, past check points, then through the last inhabited town before entering the zone cleared of civilians.

They made a piss call stop at the 38th Parallel and some cameras appeared from under their clothing and they had their pictures taken next to a sign that said: The War Began Here June 25, 1950/38th Parallel/1st Cavalry Division.

The road now paralleled a train track. There were freight cars lying alongside all jumbled with huge jagged holes torn in them. They passed medical tent cities with enormous red crosses on white backgrounds painted on the canvas roofs. Then artillery emplacements, 80mm self-propelled howitzers, 105s and 155s. And up on the slopes of the gradually narrowing valley were enormous spotlights and the tents and vehicles of the operators.

In the late afternoon they pulled into what looked like the corporation yard of a fair-sized city. It was the rail head where the Division Quartermasters unloaded the rail cars and broke down the supplies for the individual regiments and units. The Bandsmen were to provide security for this area a few miles behind the MLR.

The trucks bounced over the railroad tracks past a bare pine board guard post and stopped just the other side of the Quartermaster area at the foot of a sloping hill. They were in a narrow branch valley of the larger one they'd driven up that day.

These hills were sparsely covered with brush and scrubby evergreens. A dirty dusty snow covered the ground. It was dry, more like dirt than snow. Across the road were the foundations only of a once rather sizable village.

The men and boys crawled stiffly down from the trucks. They were told they had but an hour or two of daylight to pitch the squad tents before dark and then they could eat.

Some soldiers unloaded packs and duffel bags still filled with their summer issue from the baggage truck. Others pulled out and staked the squad tents working as quickly as possible in the darkening valley.

They erected the tents, set up cots inside on the frozen ground, took their mess kits and trooped down the road to the Quartermaster mess tent where they would get their rations and then eat sitting on the ground, or they could take it back to their tents.

It was here that Tom would get the absolutely worst meals of his Army experience. He never knew if it was the incompetence or indifference of this particular set of cooks. Quartermaster should have had a better chance than the other units at the rations but there were granular dried eggs with a greenish tint, thin bluish dried milk, woefully stale bread, slight portions of meatloaf, beef of impossible toughness, canned vegetables that were coarse and broken, canned figs that no one ate, ever.

Those soldiers with contacts at home came to rely more and more on the salamis and jars of cheese spread, gefilte fish, crackers and cookies. The Poles from the midwest got the heaviest packages. Then came the Jews and Italians of the east coast. The Wasps continued to get crumbled cookies and commercial fruit cakes.

Once Tom got a brick of Velveeta from an aunt. Another time a box of chocolate flavor drink mix and several issues of Colliers and The Saturday Evening Post from a girl named Joyce who had written to him infrequently about her job in a photography studio and how little there was to do with all the boys from town away in the Army.

Tom was at the site of the village of Taegwani at the head of the Chorwon Valley. Men were detailed to guard duty, for KP, and the rest of the Band was told to dig the tents into the side of the slope of the hill.

The tents were taken down, the men provided with picks and shovels and the frozen earth was attacked with a will. Everyone seemed persuaded that aside from providing a level tent floor they liked the idea of less exposure in the event of an artillery or mortar attack, especially as they'd seen the awesome results of such bombardments on the journey north, the carnage visited on structures and equipment.

The earth was frozen solid as granite. It yielded itself only in crumbling bits. Fortunately, there were plenty of hands to spell the workers.

The work proceeded slowly. The men rotated on and off guard duty. One group digging in their tent completed two-thirds of the job when much to their disgust they dug into an abandoned latrine pit. They had to lug all their gear down to the end of the row of tents and begin anew.

The Bandsmen dug their latrine trenches. Defecating became the single most uncomfortable thing Tom has to do. Layers of clothing were unbuttoned, undone, hiked up, pulled down. Crouched at the edge of the trench he tried to avoid soiling himself or any of the trailing clothing that was hoisted or pulled aside. And it was bitter cold.

As it turned out there was little for the Bandsmen to do. They had only two guard posts to man, a few KPs to provide. It was too cold really to schedule make work. Tom took to exploring. There was a tent of Korean labor corps personnel up a ravine several hundred yards away. They cooked over open fires and solicited laundry jobs and other tasks such as boot polishing. And further up past them was some kind of dump where small arms ammunition had been discarded. Bandoleers of M1 clips, ammunition boxes for machine guns, .45 caliber rounds. It was quite a topic of conversation. Some were concerned that it was dated or unsafe from exposure. Some decided to try firing it to see what happened. Tom took some of the cloth bandoleers of M1 rounds and draped them over and across his shoulders. He filled up his canvas ammo belt. Someone fired a few rounds of carbine ammo. Tom fired the M1. Later someone came up with a .45 caliber grease gun and they all took turns chopping up heavy wooden ammunition boxes with the rapid fire. The ravine became an impromptu firing range for a few days. Tom never learned how all that ammunition came to be there.

He climbed the hills above the tents. They were laced with shallow trenches and crude bunkers that must have been hastily formed and abandoned as they were insubstantial affairs consisting of a five-foot hole covered with pine logs, dirt, and rocks. There was no debris, ration cans, ammo casings. There was considerable barbed wire.

Occasionally units passed through their area. Once a tank company bivouacked across the road and provided a picture opportunity.

One dark, slatey grey afternoon the Bandsmen were trucked with their instruments to some regiment or battalion to play a retreat. It was so cold that Tom's saxophone reed froze. Spit valves froze. The trombone slides froze. The Bandsmen were able to produce but a few toots and squeaks to accompany the cadence of the drums. The Bandsmen thrust their freezing fingers under their armpits and waited for the trucks to take them back to their tents.

The nights on guard duty were made eerie by the search lights that illumined the dark as with an icy moonlight. They were intended to provide illumination of the MLR. Initially Tom believed that the glow helped him see but then as time passed the light created more deceptive shadows than the natural light did. Perhaps the spotlights would show vehicular, truck, or tank movement but in looking over his sector it provided Tom with the unnerving view of a squad of men creeping toward his post. Maybe as many as a company, frozen just at the moment he thought he detected a bit of motion. Tom had two choices. He could strain with every effort to see, or he could remain totally indifferent. Sometimes Tom would sight his rifle toward some object, his breath coming shallower and faster. Then he would drop his aim, lean the M1 against the wall of the guard post and concentrate only on remaining awake and on clenching and unclenching his toes and fingers to try to maintain circulation.

The men started remaining in their sleeping bags as much as possible. Most skipped breakfast and then the word was sent down that the tent sergeants would see to it that the residents of their tents would eat breakfast and that precipitated much nervous energy, resentment, and anger because there was nothing to do upon arising. But it looked bad for the Bandsmen to be lying on their cots in sleeping bags, really the only way to keep warm.

They were told that during the day they could sit on their cots but not lie on them. The time passed exceedingly slowly.

Then one day someone checked out shotguns and shells from Special Services. Tom had no idea where and how this was accomplished but some bird hunters from Wisconsin and Minnesota did it and came back with half a dozen pheasants. The unoccupied grain fields in the zone prohibited to civilians behind the MLR reseed themselves and there was an incredible abundance of game birds, rabbits, and tiny pigmy deer with odd tusk-like teeth. Once a deer ran through the tent area with everyone blazing away with their small arms. It was only luck that no one was injured including the bounding, leaping deer which streaked through unscathed.

At any rate the hunters cleaned the birds, let them

hang a few days, sectioned them, and fried them in lard obtained from the Quartermaster cooks in mess kits over a tent stove. Tom ate some of a bird, a half. It was delicious, crisp, juicy, flavorsome.

There were other semi-culinary efforts as well. There were several five-gallon water cans with dried fruit, bread, and sugar in them percolating gently in the corners of several tents back behind and under draped concealment. After a week or so a whiff of the contents indicated there was indeed some alcoholic mess that had resulted. The ferment was strained through several pairs of clean socks into canteen cups and tested by the interested parties. It was alcoholic but ghastly. Tom had no enthusiasm for drinking enough to become drunk. No one did really. It was drunk by several soldiers only. The rest abstained.

The novelty still of Korea and of his situation and the cold left Tom not missing alcohol or females. His body and urges seemed buried some vast distance away in layers of cotton and woolen underwear, field pants, sweaters, pile liners, woolen and fatigue shirts, field jacket and overcoat. Tom was one of the 20 or so Bandsmen still without parkas.

One of Tom's acquaintances, an outspoken, quirky sort of loner got into trouble with the Company Commander and the First Sergeant. Back in Louisiana the circus band earnings had gone to purchase a reel-to-reel wire recorder so that the money would benefit the whole band and not just the circus band performers. There had been some resentment on the part of the musicians who had volunteered for the circus band and its evening and weekend performances because of the opportunity for extra pay implied but then denied.

Recordings of the 45th Band had been made on this recorder and then mailed back to a radio station in Oklahoma City and played as part of a Sunday evening salute to our boys. And then from Japan as well on an increasingly intermittent basis. In the packing and crating and organizing of company property to be sent to Korea the wire recorder, a very expensive item, was crated and shipped back to Oklahoma. There was mostly indifference to its fate but an exception was the quirky individual who asked about it and investigated and kept bringing the matter up in conversation until it was learned, or at least widely believed, and it was probably true, that the CO had sold the recorder to the 1st Sergeant for a nominal price. It was the quirky soldier's assertion that a very terrible wrong had been done thereby to all the Bandsmen, the CO and 1st Sergeant excepted. He was totally indiscreet in his assertion and complaints and totally unsuccessful in persuading the other Bandsmen to join him in confronting the CO or in complaining about the CO to some higher authority.

Then one afternoon a weapons carrier with an engineer battalion designation on its bumper appeared. The quirky one was told to gather his gear. He was transferred to the combat engineers. In a daze he gathered his belongings, said goodbye to the half dozen soldiers in the tent and was driven away to the engineer outfit where that very afternoon he was helping clear a mine field and the matter of the wire recorder was settled apparently for once and for all.

One of the things in retrospect that seems interesting was Tom's lack of information about the conduct of the war and the fortunes of his own Division. There was a Division newspaper of some four pages that Tom read occasionally with some news of the action the Division involved itself in, scores of softball games played by units in reserve, news of R&R experiences, but Tom continued to live moment by moment with no anticipation of future events, reflections on but few past experiences. If ever there was an example of live one day at a time this was it.

At night there was the crump of mortars up ahead, the rustle and crackle of artillery overhead and disconnected rattles of automatic weapons fire, the pops and cracks of rifle fire. Tom never knew what the significance of any of it was. It was usually fairly distant, the sounds traveling through the biting night air.

CHAPTER 20

Tom finally decided to do something about the injustice done to his quirky acquaintance. He hiked to Division Headquarters some two miles away and asked to see the Inspector General, the IG, at a squad tent in a complex of tents again at the base of a line of hills, the tents in a semi-circle with a flag pole and a helicopter landing pad in the middle.

A grey-haired older gentleman looking awkward in the way some officers did in their laundered and starched fatigues appeared. He as a light colonel. He was smoking a pipe and wore gold rimmed glasses. He very quietly and courteously asked how he could be of service and Tom told him the full story of the wire recorder as best he knew, about the circus band and the purchase of the recorder and its sale and the perfidy of the CO who sent a Bandsman to a mine detail. His story struck Tom as a sad one and tears started to his eyes as he projected the terrible things that could happen to his untrained friend in a mine field.

The IG listened attentively until Tom was quite finished. He certainly was a good listener. He sucked on his pipe, removed it and spoke.

"It was," he said in his quiet and thoughtful way, "apparent from the story that there was an irreconcilable conflict between the quirky soldier and the CO. That in a situation such as this the best solution would be a physical separation." Then the IG looked slightly amused by his little question. "You wouldn't expect the CO to leave the Band Company, would you?" And he glanced over Tom's shoulder as he offered his hand to shake and went back to his office at the other end of the tent.

Tom walked out of the tent lightheaded almost with disappointment and the feeling of his failure to assist the quirky soldier or even to be taken seriously as he really had worked himself into a state of excitement during his uninterrupted recitation of the story.

As Tom walked back to the band area, he came to the conclusion that he would request a transfer from the band and somehow sacrifice himself as a personal witness against the injustice done his acquaintance.

The next few days Tom did little but try to formulate some plan of action that would remove him from the band and indicate his strong disapproval to the CO and 1st Sargent.

And then the opportunity came. The Division Headquarters Company Defense Platoon provided for the immediate security of the scattered tents of the Headquarters complex. The platoon manned a connected series of weapons emplacements in the hills immediately above and provided the spit and polish sentries at the war tent down by the helicopter pad.

It was decided the Defense Platoon should be real soldiers so in order that they obtain their CIBs they were assigned to infantry companies on the line for a month or so and an arrangement was made for the Bandsmen to take their places temporarily with the Defense Platoon.

Tom was told one morning that he was to spend several weeks with the platoon and the circumstances appertaining thereto and he welcomed the experience.

Tom was tired of the Band's inactivity and he wanted to get away. He thought it might be a chance to participate in the campaign as a soldier. So, Tom gathered his gear together and got into the platoon's ammo carrier and was driven away.

The driver of the vehicle was a blond kid from Oklahoma City. Tom was faintly annoyed when in the course of the conversation he learned the kid was almost a half year younger than he. Tom had come to enjoy being the youngest member of the Band Company. It had started with the amused puzzlement of the draftees who in their mid twenties contemplated a sixteen year old corporal.

Before that Tom had felt a certain anxiety lest he be discharged and returned to some relative or institution in Oklahoma to await his 17th or 18th birthday until he could rejoin some branch of the armed services. Later Tom relaxed and enjoyed the attention of the occasional soldier who would contrast what he had been doing at sixteen or seventeen with Tom's situation.

And now Tom wasn't the youngest, just one of the youngest. Thus, evaporated a small claim to fame.

And then Tom was occupied as the driver negotiated the frozen ruts in the roads between the Band Company tents and the emplacements of the Defense Platoon. The truck climbed the road into the hills above the Division Headquarters on the main road to the front. They pulled off the road at the pass through to the next valley where one of the platoon's emplacements and a checkpoint was located. There was a bunker there created from scores of sandbags. The barrel of a .30 caliber machine gun poked through a small opening in the front. An adjacent emplacement less fortified but providing some concealment held a 75mm recoilless rifle. On the back slope of the hill was a small square squad tent with fuel cans stacked at one side. Tom learned that it was a point of honor never to climb back to one's squad or even to visit another emplacement without carrying some kind of supplies because that was the most difficult part of the assignment at these positions, carrying up fuel and water.

They scrambled up a narrow icy trail bordered with lots of barbed wire, abandoned communications wire and terse little signs announcing Clear of Mines to This Point. Some parts of the trail were so steep that steps had been hacked out of the frozen earth. Tom paused to catch his breath and shift his burdens, but the driver doggedly climbed ahead. Tom put all else out of his mind by putting one foot ahead of the other.

A 30 minute climb and they reached a terrace dug 20 yards or so below the crest of the hill occupied by a small square tent that was completely surrounded by barbed wire above and below the terrace. At this place the slope was so steep the terrace had to be held by a cribbing of pine logs.

They ducked into the tent and Tom met several of the

squad members. Each squad of the platoon was under strength. Here five soldiers provided 24 hour security. Their primary weapon here was a .50 caliber machine gun set in an extraordinarily secure bunker on the slope opposite the tent. Trenches led from the tent in a zig-zag up over the slope to the bunker. Other trenches led to firing pits flanking the main bunker and barbed wire extended down the slope and in either direction to the next defensive emplacement.

Two hundred yards on past the tent the crest of the hill flattened out and there was a quad .50 mounted on a half track that was the anchor of the left flank of the defensive perimeter.

Tom was offered some coffee and learned that where they were meals were something of a problem. They would have to climb back down the hill to the check point and if they were lucky, they could catch the ammo truck to the mess tent. Otherwise it was yet another 30 minute walk. Each meal required an exhausting climb than of not less than an hour and a half and carrying a five gallon can of fuel or water the last leg of the trip back to the tent.

The cooks were sympathetic. If there were cans of rations available, they gave them to the Defense Platoon. There seemed to be plenty of bread, margarine and jam. Sometimes there were fresh eggs they could have. Most platoon members adopted the practice of eating one meal a day depending on their time on guard duty and then snacking on bread fried in margarine and flavored with jam. If the weather was especially intense, they often holed up and ate fried bread and shared out the contents of packages from home for a day or two.

They spent their time on guard duty, in the bunker, cleaning equipment, sewing, on repairs. One of the squad members had been an upholsterer and sewed tears in his clothing with an immense half moon of an upholsterer's needle waxing his thread from a white block of wax he carried in his pocket.

Because there were so few, they usually pulled guard alone. Tom could look down the slope of the hill below the machine gun emplacement to an evacuation hospital to the left with helicopters coming and going and across that valley to the line of hills that represented the MLR. There wasn't much to watch during the day, sometimes jets swooping down below the crest of the hills opposite. At night there were the searchlights with their cool pale blue light and flares floating on parachutes above the hills and tracers.

At times though during the day Tom would be joined by one or two of the Korean labor corps members who either were attached to or just hung around the Defense Platoon. They lived what seemed to Tom a very precarious life down by the river that flowed past the Division Headquarters. They had some old tents. Their clothing was a mish-mash of Korean padded jackets, combat boots or split-toed canvas shoes. They were ill clad and didn't look any too well fed.

The Koreans had a couple of 55 gallon steel drums in which they boiled the laundry they solicited. They bummed and scrounged any cast offs of any kind the platoon members contemplated discarding; cardboard boxes, emptied ration cans, anything. They didn't steal ever. They were older men in their mid-40's and older with roughened chapped hands. Some had wisps of beards on their chins. Apparently, they were incapable of picking up much English other than OK Joe. Any other communication was accomplished if at all with elaborate gestures and the acting out of short dramatizations. A few were quite gregarious but for the most part they were quiet and withdrawn. Tom was told they had been drafted into the labor corps for 12 years or the duration. If that were true, he could understand the despairing distant behavior of many of them. They did some digging and carrying, but mostly they just hung around the platoon or fooled around their own tents down by the river.

Every night the fuel line to the stove froze and the fire went out. There was one soldier who used to get up in the freezing cold and rattle around but most of them simply lay in their bags and dreaded being called for their turn at guard.

The duty schedule called for each man to stand two hours on, four hours off. Most of the soldiers slept nude. The bags seemed most effective that way, warmer. When awakened the soldiers would literally leap into the multiple layers of clothing, rubbing and chafing to warm the frozen layers.

Often their feet never did recover from the sudden chill. Feet were a major problem. You could stamp them, walk around. Somehow without warming they would perspire and then be colder than ever.

The platoon did succeed in obtaining a parka for Tom and the increase in comfort was remarkable. Never again was his upper torso chilled. Tom loved the warmth. The parka did so effectively what it was intended to do that it almost made up for the awkward inefficiency of some of the other articles of cold weather clothing. Like the goofy mittens with their field cloth shell that came up the forearms with buckles that were to be tightened and flaps and folds through which to extend a trigger finger.

Gradually Tom made his way around the other posts of the defensive perimeter to meet the other members of the platoon and just to check things out. He never did meet the platoon leader, or platoon leaders actually, a series of second lieutenants who hung around Division Headquarters.

Tom made a friend, a Cpl. York, who was the squad leader at the check point by the road and when an opening occurred in his squad, Tom made his request and was assigned there.

It was a lot handier. It wasn't as isolated and there were no fuel cans to carry. Their ammo carrier was parked there so he got to meals more often.

Tom was a lot busier here stopping vehicles to determine their business, saluting a lot of officers in their jeeps. Cpl. York tutored Tom in the operation of the emplacement's 75mm recoilless and Tom wrote down the facts he was to memorize in the back of a small black address book. The tube has 14 lands and grooves and things like that.

One afternoon the squad carried the 75mm to a hilltop and fired across a narrow valley so that Tom could sight the weapon and fire it by rotating the grip and depressing the firing button. Cpl. York stood an empty wooden ammo box behind the weapon and Tom saw the effect of the back blast. The heavy box was blown away in splinters.

In his notebook Cpl. York had Tom draw the lines of sight for the 75mm and for the .30 caliber and write in the distances in yards to the bends in the road and to the bases of the hills. This was all good stuff so Tom decided to ask for a transfer from the Band Company to the Defense Platoon and having learned the undermanned Defense Platoon would be glad to have him, Tom took an afternoon off and presented himself to the Band CO whom he hadn't seen for over a month.

Tom was asked how he was doing and if he was ready to come back to the Band. If he was, they'd ship somebody else over for a while. Tom said he was fine, that he liked the Defense Platoon, and that he was making a request for a transfer.

The CO looked at him in surprise and shook his head no. He said he'd made a promise to the community and the parents that he'd keep an eye on all the boys and bring them back alive and in one piece and that's what he intended to do.

Tom persisted in his request. The 1st Sergeant came into the tent drawn by the tone of the exchanges and laughed at Tom's request. But finally, the CO assented with an exasperated shrug, dismissing Tom and any concern for Tom's future welfare for once and for all. Tom thanked the CO, saluted, and walked out of the tent with a real sense of achievement. He checked a few of the tents to say goodbye and then made his way back to the platoon with a sense of relief and pride.

In due time the paperwork was completed, made its way around the Division and Tom had a new mailing address and a new MOS, heavy weapons specialist.

Tom heard some new stories sitting in the squad tent. Cpl. York was married, from Birmingham, Alabama. He was a steel worker. Tom was surprised to learn there was heavy industry in the South. In elementary geography he'd read the center of the steel industry was Pittsburgh because of Pennsylvania coal and the cheap transportation of ore by water while Alabama had been blanketed with cotton plantations except where the crop had been superseded by yam and peanut farms.

Tom heard more long, quiet stories about the beauties of Wisconsin and Michigan and Tom envisioned pastures and rich farms and evergreen bordered lakes where blond blue-eyed farm boys caught walleyed pike.

The powdery dry intense cold loosened its grip gradually and the snows came soft and wet. The roads were slushy and muddy. There were times in the protected south side of the tent that sleeping bags would be laid out to air and the soldiers would take off their shirts and woolen underwear tops and lie in the temporary warmth of the sun.

Their bodies were almost comically white with blue veins showing across their upper chests and arms.

As the snows retreated the frozen earth began to release and expose numerous things that had been concealed under the layers of snow and snowdrifts. Paper of all kinds dried and blew around, paper from the previous summer before the 45th had arrived to replace the 1st Cav and discarded by other units from both sides of the conflict, toilet paper, surrender leaflets with Sun Yat Sen's picture. And besides paper, turds, and in scattered areas cannisters, shrapnel, pieces of canvas, cans, and especially in one section, skeletons both in and out of trenches and bunkers. Scattered all about were bits of bodies, helmets, and skulls.

One of the Defense Platoon squads stuck a skull on a post over their tent door. Most of the soldiers avoided the areas where the bodies were concentrated, the skeletons clad in rotted uniforms, the basin-like helmets of the Chinese, the split-toed canvas shoes, because of the fear that the remains perhaps still held some kind of contagion.

Before someone got around to detailing the platoon, under the supervision of a graves registration sergeant, to picking up, Tom went once with the lone enthusiast, the treasure-souvenir hunter of the Defense Platoon.

He was a cheerful youth who might have been collecting pebbles at the beach. He scattered and turned the skeletons with his toe and went into bunkers where Tom, in horror, simply refused to follow, collecting buttons and badges. Once rather than stick his hand through a ribcage to take an enameled red star pinned to a scrap of fabric, the youth came down sharply with his heel, cracking one side open and then picked out the medal.

Tom's single souvenir was a long thin bayonet with a wooden handle. There were what he assumed to be Japanese characters and a chrysanthemum embossed on the blade below the hilt. Tom planned to give it to his brother. That would do for a souvenir as far as Tom was concerned.

He had read somewhere that souvenirs and trophies of war not certified would be confiscated on the way home so he went to a clerical tent in the Headquarters area with the bayonet and a clerk in pressed fatigues typed a description of the bayonet on a form that was then signed by a lieutenant clerk. Tom took the souvenir back to his tent, wrapped it in a towel, put it in his duffel bag, and dismissed souvenir collecting from his attention.

One day Cpl York announced he was organizing an R&R for his own squad. By standing double duties the squad could free up two men at a time for an entire day's freedom to sleep, or roam, or visit. The stress of two hours on and four off had begun to tell somewhat even on the young healthy soldiers of the Defense Platoon. Tom and the upholsterer decided to hitch hike back toward Seoul to an English Army canteen they had heard was 15 or 20 miles down the road and buy something. Tom had bought nothing since the transactions for eggs back at the repel depot and the urge to make a simple purchase had grown on him like a desire for some unobtainable food.

General Ridgeway on the other hand, and Dean Acheson, Admiral Turner Joy, and all the other military and governmental agents tortured one another in their attempts to contribute to the achievement of a stable armistice agreement with the Chinese and North Koreans. The popular impression is their agreement on a demarcation line will end the fighting. Not so. What is ahead is 18 months of negotiation over the disposition of prisoners of war.

Each soldier received a free cigarette ration. Tom chainsmoked except when on guard two or three packs of Camels a day. They received a beer or Coca Cola ration of two cans a week. There had been more beer available at first, but Tom read of some flap in Congress about all the cargo space and manpower involved in distributing beer to the troops and then in the 45th there were incidents of drunkedness at listening posts, even out in front of the lines. One entire squad had been killed in their sleeping bags which they weren't supposed to have there in the first place and there had been cases of beer, not just a few cans, consumed and still unconsumed in the bunker. This really POed the Division Commander who said from now on two cans a week for the enlisted men of the Division.

There were a surprising number of nondrinkers. They could sell or give away their beer ration, so it was still possible with planning to accumulate six or eight cans to get drunk. Tom hadn't bothered. A combination of things left him indifferent; the cold, hunger, exhaustion.

At any rate, they left the checkpoint at 8:00 AM and walked down the hill and out of the Headquarters area for the first time in a long while to a long straight gravel road leading south and hitch hiking obtained a series of short rides on, in, and about a variety of vehicles. Around 11:00 AM they reached a field hospital complex where they'd been told there was an open mess and anyone who wished could eat. They walked up the drive from the main road and became conscious of the contrast between their appearance and that of the soldiers and officers at the hospital. Tom and his friend still wore shoepacks, the others wore boots or flimsy-looking low cuts. They wore parkas, the others wore field jackets with the slick newness of them that had not had much contact with the ground. They wore helmets, the others field caps. They carried M1s and wore ammo belts with a bayonet, first aid packet, canteen, and full ammo pouches. A few of the officers there wore .45s on their web belts, the EM went unarmed.

Tom looked at his friend's face and while the soldiers at the hospital looked relaxed and rested and pinkish clean, his friend had dark circles around his eyes and when he removed his helmet his hair was matted and dry. The other guy's hair was combed and in the fashion of the 50's it shone with oil. There were freshly shaved necks. So much for the differences. The thing that embarrassed Tom the most was how filthy he and his friend were in contrast to the others in the mess tent. They had leaned against and lain in dirt bunkers, oil had spilled on them when changing empty fuel cans for full ones. Grime was ground into their clothing, their hands, wrists, and faces. They took metal food trays and tableware and stood in the short chow line.

They had taken their canteen cups out but there were china coffee cups.

They felt bulky and dirty and tried to arrange their wild matted hair with a free hand. They took their filled trays to an unoccupied bench and leaned their M1s against the table and put their helmets on the wooden floor of the mess tent and while they ate looked at the other soldiers sitting easily, chatting over their meals and coffee cups and cigarettes. To Tom's shocked surprise there were officers eating seated next to enlisted men and female nurses in fatigues laughing. It was strange. In his Division the officers and enlisted men were strictly segregated for all body functions; sleeping, eating, shitting.

A group of four soldiers joined them at the table, nodded politely, and asked where they were from. Tom felt ill at ease, his tongue seemed thick, he was inarticulate, and when the soldiers noticed how ill at ease, he appeared they politely turned away and chatted about hospital gossip. Tom and the upholsterer found where the trays and cups were to be returned, buckled up and left the mess tent with much more than food for subsequent conversations. The experience had provided them with a sort of benchmark for comparing how different their everyday experiences had become from their previous ones in Japan and the U.S. The further south they got the less frequently rides were offered them. An hour's walk brought them to their destination, the English canteen.

It was a small tar papered building. Inside there was little to buy on the mostly empty shelves. They each had a cup of tea with milk and sugar in a large stained white china cup. They were served by an English soldier wearing a huge woolen jacket and a beret. Tom finally decided on some English cigarettes and a box of soap powder.

Then it was time to start home. They trudged along the road. The dust was thick after each vehicle that passed. They had little luck getting rides. Once a short jeep convoy stopped. They looked at the lead jeep loaded with MPs in fancy gear. There was a .30 caliber machine gun mounted in the back seat. From the front seat of the second jeep in line a vigorous middle-aged man gestured them over. He was spectacular, there were four silver stars across the front of his helmet. Tom and the upholsterer saluted hastily and stood at attention. The driver of the jeep was impressive in a stainless steel helmet, maybe it was chrome. There was a red plaque with four silver stars on the bumper of the jeep and pennants on the front fenders. The general had hand grenades hanging from his field jacket breast pockets. His fatigue pants shone with starch. He pulled himself forward in his seat with one hand, returned Tom's salute and asked how they were. They replied, "Just fine, Sir." He asked what outfit they were within the 45th and he told Tom that General Doughtery was a personal friend and a fine fighting man. He told them he was proud of the fine job their Division was doing and to keep up the good work. Then he gestured to his driver and they saluted and the general saluted looking them right in the eye and they remained at attention for a moment longer as the little convoy drove off at high speed leaving a hell of a dust trail of finely powdered yellow grit.

They decided that must have been General Ridgeway and for the second time that day they were impressed by the cleanliness and polish of those whose soldiering took them in a different direction.

They got back to their tent and lay down glad to be back home among the familiar barbed wire and bunkers. Tom smoked his English cigarettes. The soap powder sat by his cot until he finally gave it to one of the Koreans.

CHAPTER 21

One morning around 3:00 AM Tom was awakened by sirens first, and then Cpl. York rushing into the tent shouting there was a full alert with all the Division Headquarters personnel rousted out and hurrying up the hill on foot to take positions in the trenches between the bunkers.

Tom wrenches the machine gun from its tripod and leaps to the roof of the bunker. He holds the weapon at pubic bone level and spits fire at the enemy. He shreds the mustard-colored padded uniforms to bloody rags. He is afraid of the enemy. He doesn't want them to suffer needless pain. He runs toward the fallen men and boys and fires at their heads at point blank range. Blood and bone are all over his boots. He thinks: I am too close to this, I must keep my distance. I don't enjoy this.

The Defense Platoon was to act as traffic cops as well as man the heavy weapons at each post. Tom had no more than thrown on his clothes when the first clerks arrived in helmets, carrying carbines, and requesting instructions and directions. Tom sent them up the paths, parceling them out four at a time telling them where to find the trenches and firing pits and telling them to watch out for barbed wire and not to stray into areas not clear of mines and booby traps, just about any place off the path. Flares were fired off one after the other. The soldiers sorting themselves out were ill at ease and wanted to know what was expected of them when they got to the trenches. Tom told them they would simply await orders. There was some cursing at the checkpoint by a couple of excited officers who insisted the soldiers hustle it up and run. But running in the semi-darkness involved so much jostling and stumbling that the movement generated by the officers' abuse extended only a dozen yards on either side of them.

In a half hour, things sorted out and several hundred men sat crouched in trenches with carbines between their knees wondering what the hell was really going on and whether it was OK to light a cigarette or to call out quietly to locate an acquaintance.

The officers huffed and puffed up and down the defensive perimeter no curses on their lips now. After another hour of intense silence one of the officers blew a whistle and the men filed out of the trenches and straggled back down the hill to their office tents smoking cigarettes and still asking questions. Tom never knew the reason for all that activity. There were several possible explanations, a few loose gooks, a practice alert. No one ever came up with an explanation for all that commotion.

Tom went to the tent to undress and go back to bed when the soldier on duty came in and said it was Tom's turn on guard in 10 minutes. Tom sat on his cot and smoked another cigarette. He went out to the sand-bagged check point and sleepily watched the sky turn from black to grey, and a whitish-blue with several stars still visible, and then whiter and yellower, and the day began.

There were lots of rabbits foraging in the hills. It was startling at first as they rustled in the dry brush that had grown up in the barbed wire in front of their position. Tom feared it was caused by the movement of deadly snakes of which they'd received official warnings in pamphlets and that whole deal made the experience of entering trenches and bunkers and negotiating the rocky terrain such an ordeal and kept Tom slightly on edge and jittery. The barbed wire was laced with trip wires that set off phosphorous flares and from time to time a small animal, usually a rabbit would set off one of these things that burned itself out in a cloud of intensely irritating smoke.

One afternoon a flare was ignited below the machine gun bunker and started a small brush fire. To avoid any possible trouble if the fire spread Tom took an empty sandbag, saturated it with water from a water can and started through the barbed wire climbing over and through it to reach the burning brush. As Tom was pulling his jacket loose from a section of wire in which he'd become entangled a phosphorous flare went off at his feet and he was enveloped in a thick cloud of smoke that burned and choked with his first startled breath.

Tom pulled, tugged, and thrashed his way free of the wire but not before he'd involuntarily taken another lung full that had burned all the way down. Tom was crying and choking when he pulled himself into the fresh air just a moment after the accident. His eyes were tearing. He couldn't see. He was afraid the cloud would reach him again. He was caught in the wire several more times, but he struggled up the slope until he was out of the wire and reached the bunker where he could find the water can to splash water in his eyes and on his face.

It hurt to breathe, his chest hurt. He sat breathing shallowly, really worried that maybe he'd been seriously injured. He made his way to the tent and Cpl. York assigned someone to take Tom's guard and drove Tom in the ammo carrier to the medics' tent. He insisted that Tom be seen by a doctor, not just a medic, right away in case there was some timely treatment that would prevent any serious injury. The doctor came in, a quietly relaxed captain, who examined Tom's eyes and throat and then looked away as he said he would give Tom some ointment to relieve the eye irritation, but that Tom would probably have a sore throat for a while. It didn't appear to be very serious, but Tom could drop by again if any additional problems developed.

The captain showed Tom how to squeeze the ointment from its metal tube into his eye and that sensation was so unpleasant and involved such awkward games with himself to keep himself from squinting hard that Tom discarded the tube the same day.

It hurt to breathe deeply for a long time after that. Tom lost his appetite and in a strange way his appetite or interest in a number of other things as well. He didn't feel like talking, of course smoking was not pleasurable, but he did keep that up.

The warming weather brought an end to foot inspection. During cold weather medics inspected their feet once a week. Tom's toes naturally spread so widely the medic didn't have to pull them apart as he had to do with most of the other soldiers. When Tom spread his toes, the medic would laugh and say he appreciated not having to handle at least one pair of dirty feet each week.

Also, with the warmer weather was the often repeated advice on how to avoid the scorpions, centipedes, and poisonous snakes which supposedly abounded in the ideal habitat of rocky hills and stream beds. It continued to be a real source of anxiety, but Tom never saw to his great relief any reptiles. They were supposed to be incredibly aggressive and venomous after the winter's hibernation. Their bites almost guaranteed certain death of an Oriental severity.

Further past the Defense Platoon perimeter were a number of Korean gravesites. These were circular mounds on small terraces placed randomly in the hills, usually on slopes that were treeless. Often there was a granite stele. Tom wondered what might be found if the grave were dug into.

Once on a short hike down into a wooded ravine Tom encountered a wooden shrine perhaps six by five with an entire roof. Looking through a type of grill in the door he saw an altar. He was surprised at finding anything whole and apparently not vandalized. Every other human construction so far consisted only of outlines of foundations and a bit of scattered rubble. Tom said nothing of his discovery in the hope that it could somehow survive the events and consequences of the police action.

Once examining the foundations of some houses in the village site on the river with a more knowledgeable companion it was pointed out to Tom that the terra cotta pipes running beneath the house, now exposed in bits and broken pieces had circulated heated air under the homes of the relatively well-off. Tom was also told the Koreans were master potters and ceramicists and their skill and art had been admired and studied by the Chinese and Japanese. That was about the extent of Tom's knowledge of Korean culture. He did know there was a Syngman Rhee who had an American education and was a fierce patriot.

Tom felt sorry for the middle-aged Koreans of the labor camps with their ragged padded uniforms and sour garlicky smell that he was told was the consequence of eating a fiery condiment, a kind of vegetable pickle called Kimchee.

He was less sympathetic toward the contingent of Korean MPs that lived a quarter mile past the Defense Platoon check point. They had some responsibilities at the field hospital below. He could see the toilet paper strewn slope below the MP's tent. They didn't bother digging latrine trenches. Tom had a run-in with them when a group of four that included two staggering drunks wanted to walk past the check point into the Division Headquarters area one night. They had arrogantly ignored his initial verbal challenge and they had turned back only when Tom had slammed a round into his weapon after he unslung it and held it at port arms. The Korean MPs bullied the labor corps' workers whenever their paths chanced to cross.

Division Headquarters tended to be a fairly lively place as the weather improved. Sometimes the sound of popular music drifted up to the defensive perimeter. At chow in the mess tent Tom overheard stories of officers' parties in the complex of tents around the Division CO's tent and the senior officers' mess tent. The Division Band had resumed sending an entertainment unit to the general several nights a week. Visiting USO and Special Services groups made it through also.

One morning around 1:00 AM or so a jeep came roaring up the hill emitting loud singing and shrill American female laughter as it bounced past the check point where Tom was standing guard. Ten minutes later it came speeding back in return with explosive halloos and shouts of piercing coarseness. It seemed to Tom so cheap to flaunt that behavior and privilege in front of an anonymous doggie. It didn't please him. That particular evening must have been the culmination of some social process because when Tom was assigned guard duty at the war tent the next week everything was decorous and military and there were no sights or sounds of the previous entertainments.

Tom had not looked forward to the war tent assignment. The war tent was the location of the sandbox representation of the Chorwon sector and where the Division CO met with the unit commanders to plan the Division actions and reactions to the events of the day.

It was a duty shared in rotation by the Defense Platoon members who regarded it as a strict pain in the neck. First off, Tom had to arrange to get his best set of fatigues laundered, starched, and ironed by one of the Korean launderers. He had to GI all his webbed gear, spit polish his boots, clean and wipe down his M1 until it shone, wear a blue silk scarf under his neck and wear a special shiny helmet liner with the words Defense Platoon imprinted across the front. He was to stand at attention or parade rest during each two hour shift. During the day there was much coming and going and each individual or group received his present arms. Some acknowledged it, others simply passed by with their folders and attache cases.

The helicopter pad was busy and drivers in jeeps sprawled in their seats awaiting their next excursion.

Then the Commanding General of the 45th, an Oklahoman, was rotated home and was replaced by a squat, red-faced two star general who raised hell with the troops. From now on everyone on the line wore flak jackets. And everyone, much to the disgust of the troops off the line had to wear a steel helmet. This was war, goddammit. In the rear it had been the custom to wear field caps or helmet liners. First off everybody knows wearing a steel helmet shuts off circulation to the scalp and causes premature baldness. Some soldiers were seen by the general breaking the rule. They were identified, busted, fined, put on the bottom of their unit's rotation list. Everyone subsequently lowered his neck under a steel helmet.

At the end of March, spring was over, and it was summer; hot, dry, still dusty. Tom once thought of swimming in the wide shallow river that flowed through their valley, but the warnings he'd read about it and the awful things he'd seen in and around the river persuaded him to leave it alone.

One afternoon Cpl. York came into the tent and said a shower tent had been set up a few miles away and that they could take the ammo carrier and go get a shower. Tom's last shower had been in Japan, the morning of the October day on which they'd left and there had been no other opportunity to bathe in the six months he'd now been in Korea. Tom and four others drove down the MSR and stopped at a group of tents surrounded by trucks and portable generators. A line of troops a hundred yards long was waiting to get into one of the tents. Vehicles were parked all over. It was like a county fair or circus. When Tom's group made its way into the tent, they were told to take off their fatigues, underwear, and socks and throw them into large canvas bins. Wearing only helmets and boots, carrying weapons, web gear, and personal items, they walked through to another tent where they piled their possessions in heaps and were given bars of soap. They filed into the shower tent with a floor of duck boards and Tom shared a shower head with a half dozen other soldiers, soaping up and rinsing off repeatedly in the stream of lukewarm water. The place became more crowded with new arrivals. Leaving the shower tent Tom was handed a towel and after drying off he went to a counter where he was given clean underwear, socks, and fatigues. The pants were newer and in better condition than the ones he'd turned in. The jacket had been torn and was roughly mended. The clothing had been run through a mangle and felt wonderfully cool and crisply clean. It was a strange sensation to feel completely clean all over. Tom had washed in the months before with a soapy washcloth but the sensation of warm soapy water on his back had been a deep pleasure.

With the weather warm they rolled up the sides of their squad tent and lying on his cot Tom could look down upon Division Headquarters and across the valley to the scrub covered hills shimmering in the early summer heat. Whenever a breeze sprang up it was lazily comfortable to watch the coming and going of vehicles on the dusty roads below.

One afternoon lying idly on his cot Tom was unhappy to realize that he was about to wonder about returning to Oklahoma. The first guardsmen had begun their departures. And while there were only a few of the original guardsmen still in the Defense Platoon when Tom had transferred, he'd been placed at the bottom of the Headquarters Company rotation list.

The next day two Oklahomans left. A returnee usually had only a day or two's notice of the actual date of departure. When one got his official notice, it was the custom to buy a fifth of liquor from an officer or intermediary for $25, then to go to each of the four defensive positions and share the bottle with the drinkers.

Tom had held a bottle to his mouth a couple of times while it burned his lips and he'd pretended to drink and then expressed extreme satisfaction. The person leaving always offered to carry messages, run errands, or such for those remaining behind. They always faithfully promised to journey to Detroit, or Birmingham, or Hartford when all this was over and in turn, they were promised fried chicken, or kielbasa, or rigatoni of exquisite deliciousness, and introductions to blondes, brunettes, or fishing trips, country pleasure, city delights.

They all left and to Tom's acute interest they were replaced by Black draftees; young, tall, skinny, affable, gregarious, eastern. President Truman was integrating the Army and as the white Oklahomans left the Division they were replaced in large part by savvy young Blacks who took an interest in what was going on and settled in right away in their new homes with stories about their adventures in basic training and their journey to Korea. They were quick to offer cigarettes or to lend items of equipment and those assigned to the Defense Platoon were mightily relieved as would a newcomer of any Race to learn their position in the geography of war: That the enemy was not to be found on the visible mountain opposite, but on the next mountain over past the one you could see with yet another valley besides the one below them intervening.

So Tom wondered what it would be like after he left Korea. He didn't want to return to the United States. He wanted to stay in Japan or perhaps Okinawa. He'd heard that was good duty. He wanted to stay somewhere in the Orient.

One afternoon Cpl. York told Tom it was his turn and Tom would be leaving in two days. This was a message of such serious import that Tom's lack of any kind of response caused the corporal to ask him if he wasn't glad. Tom said, "Yes, of course." York said he envied him and he'd be damn glad to get home himself and offered to get Tom a bottle of liquor from the platoon leader, the price was $25. And sure enough, that night Tom had a cool brown bottle of Canadian Club that some young lieutenant had brought back from Japan in his suitcase. It was time for his goodbye party. Tom was glad to be leaving Korea. He just didn't want to go home.

After supper Tom took the bottle with him and spent a few minutes at the farthest position down on the right flank of the perimeter. Tom didn't know those members of the platoon that well. It was a long hike out there. It was the wildest, wooliest part of the sector with the most skeletons and debris still on the back slope. The guys out there had the reputation for being kind of weird. Tom left with their good wishes.

At the next bunker Tom watched with fascinated apprehension as a Black soldier drank from the bottle and then handed it to a white. No problem. The white guy wiped the mouth of the bottle on his sleeve and took a drink. Tom was proffered the usual invitations to Wisconsin and Connecticut and made his way to the post of his original assignment way up the hill on the other side of the road. By now it was dark. The night was warm. They sat on the cots and drank. Tom was drinking now forcing down little drafts and smoking furiously to ease the nausea and unpleasant tightness in his jaws. He was salivating heavily. But as time went on Tom relaxed as it was easier to get the small swallows of liquor down and keep them down. They watched Tom drink. His face and forehead grew numb. He neglected the quiet conversation. He had several cigarettes lighted. His mouth was open. He heard his breath whistling between his teeth. He felt a surging dizziness and decided to get out of the tent. He pushed himself to his feet. He heard some disconnected words. He felt hands grasp at his arms and as he pulled free, he fell forward out of the tent. He was on his hands and knees. He was on his feet again. He took several steps in the dark and then his leading foot went away, down, and he fell for a moment and then there was a powerful crushing pressure. Tom rolled and stopped in a sticky batch of wire, and he slept.

He was awakened with the feeling of his arms being pulled. He was pulled to his feet. It was light but very early in the morning. Tom wanted a drink of water and a cigarette. He ached.

He heard a voice saying, "One of the sergeants said you were so drunk when you walked off the terrace, he didn't think you'd hurt yourself, so we thought we'd just let you sleep."

Tom looked back up the slope to the log parapet, at the height he'd fallen, at the distance he'd rolled, at the barbed wire that had caught and held him. He felt lucky he hadn't broken a bunch of bones in his body.

They helped him back up to the trail. He looked down at his clothing and decided he'd had enough goodbye party.

Tom shook hands and took himself carefully down the steep trail for the last time and marveled at how quickly this episode in his life had passed.

Tom left behind with the company; his parka, sleeping bag, M1, and his webbed gear. He had only his duffel bag. He said his goodbyes. He was driven in the ammo carrier down to the Headquarters Company clerk's tent and was given a sheaf of orders. Tom told the driver he'd walk from there over to the rail head.

Tom walked over to the Quartermaster depot and the train where there were 50 or 60 rotatees standing, waiting, joking. He recognized some hoodlum crazies from an artillery outfit out of some small town in western Oklahoma. This group of soldiers standing by the train was the very last group of National Guardsmen to leave the Division. Many of them were in this last contingent because of disciplinary problems they'd caused, or fuckups, or guys like Tom who'd transferred. Even the quirky sergeant had made it out before this group, of which, Tom was a member.

Then Tom saw a Bandsman he'd known pretty well and liked even though they hadn't palled around much. They were glad to see each other. It was good to have an acquaintance to share the trip back home with. Tom asked questions about the Band until a sergeant appeared who told them to fall in. Their names were called and then they climbed into a railway car attached to a freight train headed back to Seoul.

The ride was not unpleasant. The day was hot, but the

windows were wide open. They unlaced their boots and joked, and yelled, and waved at the passing scene. In a half hour or so they saw their first civilian working in a field who stopped hoeing and looked up at the passing train. They passed by villages now seeing women and especially children for the first time in eight months.

They exchanged rumors that some of them, or all of them, would be flown back to the United States, or that they were going to Hawaii to be processed and could take a week's leave time there if they wished. They yelled happy obscenities at the women they saw and grabbed their crotches. They wondered when they would get to where they were going and what they would have to eat, and when.

A crap game or two was started. Others played cards arguing about closing the windows so the cards wouldn't blow around. Tom grew quiet again concerned about how he should go about doing whatever a serviceman did to remain in the Orient. He had just about decided to remain in the Army. He saw no possibilities for himself out of the Army, alone and without resources, not even a plan.

He rode down the valley from Chorwon and through the devastation outside Seoul, inching across a railroad bridge, then stopping. They left the train and stood by the track for another roll call, climbed into trucks to be taken to the replacement depot with the fenced in mess tent and the crowd of onlookers with the outstretched hands.

Climbing down from the truck they were told to fall in for another roll call. They were told where to draw bedding and their tent assignments. Tom and his friend from the Band stuck together the day-and-a-half they spent at Yongdongpo smoking and lying on their cots. A sergeant told them they were in a funnel that collected soldiers who were returning to the States from the Far East, and it led to the States but that it required processing through a number of staging areas until a boatload of them finally converged in the right place at the right time. They should all be home in a month or so.

Frequent roll calls, a few soldiers detailed out for fire watch or KP, and then back on the trucks to the railroad yard for the next leg of the trip. This time it was the third class rail carriages with inverted T wooden seats. They groused and bitched and grew rather ill-tempered from discomfort.

They continued south through manure and feces smelling rice paddies, always hills on either side. Past switchboxes and little wooden sheds with gangs of Korean railroad employees in dusty black or blue uniforms and always the rubber shoes with the turned up toes.

Once the train stopped for some reason or other in the rail yard of a small city and beggars converged of the train, mostly old women holding up their arms to the windows of the railcars. One old woman neither more nor less pathetic than the rest had a small cloth purse in her hand which one of the artillery crazies grabbed, pulled it back into the train and opened to see what was in it. It contained a few paper bills of a total worth of 15 or 20 cents. Crazy tore them up and tossed the purse out the opposite window and laughed at the old woman's consternation, her lamentations, her fearful final decision not to try crawling under the car to retrieve her purse on the other side. Tom had leaned forward in disbelief when the incident began, but then sat back and gazed away from the crazy soldier who was loudly inquiring if anyone had seen the totally disgusting thing he had done.

Tom and the other soldiers ate small cans of rations heated in an immersion heater sitting at one end of the car.

The next stop was Taijon. They stayed in what must have been a secondary school made of yellow brick. Tall shade trees made it cool and pleasant in the open gravelled space where the soldiers assembled. Tom met soldiers from units other than those from the 45th for the first time, the 3rd Division, from a regimental combat team, I Corps. There was an air of permanence about this facility, no tents. The food wasn't bad. They were told they could change from fatigues into cooler khakis if they had them. There were Korean laundresses all over the place and they could get their laundry done in half a day.

It was odd wearing crisply starched khakis after a hot shower. Tom bought shoe polish and polished his low cuts. He blitz-clothed his brass and belt buckle. It helped to pass the time which otherwise was spent in napping and dozing. One of the sergeants there sang a funny song about how in the event of an atomic war the regular Army noncoms would be protected by the lead in their ass. This was for the benefit of a group of older regular Army sergeants who were being assigned to Korea from duty in the United States and Japan in response to some kind of political pressure.

They were older guys who'd stayed in after WWII. Many had families. They'd had desk or warehouse jobs at regular Army installations. They were soft and white for the most part. They didn't wear their new field gear with any sort of familiarity. Many were balding and paunchy. Tom wondered what was in store for them and how they'd manage later on. Most were sergeants in the top grades. They sat or assembled in a mild almost civilian kind of awkwardness Tom had not seen since the draftees came in at Camp Polk.

A half-dozen more roll calls and Tom and the others were assembled and trucked to the railyards for the next leg to Taegu.

The day was hot and dry and then it was nighttime. They were rocked and jolted indifferent to anything in the landscape. They had already seen rice paddies, mist wagons, poverty, thin people in rags, destroyed warehouses, trucks, hills, switchmen, sluggish rivers, MPs, hay ricks. They sat gazing but not reflecting on anything that chanced to be visible. Or else they slept heavy sleeps awakening to urinate or smoke cigarettes and then sleep again.

Now there was no excitement or anticipation about going home, or if there was it occurred now only occasionally and was nothing that was held at high pitch during the hours of traveling, and waiting, and standing in formation to answer, "Ho," when a name was called.

They arrived in Taegu during hours of darkness, sometime after midnight. They went by truck to a kind of

Army town of wooden barracks where early the next morning they went through a series of buildings for physicals, interviews, counseling and inspections.

At the first building they were obliged to dump the contents of their duffel bags on long tables where fast talking soldiers sorted through their belongings. Tom didn't like this, especially when a corporal unwrapped his souvenir bayonet, the gift for his brother, and tossed it behind him into a bin and said curtly, "Illegal, you can't keep this." Tom said, "Hold it, I got the proper paper," which he located in his sheaf of orders. The corporal reluctantly surrendered it and then took a field cap Tom had bought in Japan and said you won't need DDs anymore. Tom let the cap go wondering what kind of racket these guys were working on the tired and apathetic rotatees. They were probably supposed to screen the troops' belongings for contraband, but they were bluffing and taking whatever struck their fancy. Again, Tom had to contrast the dulled acceptance of the behavior of the venal con by the troops being rotated with the aggressive self-interest in the game these rested, bored, rear echelon troops exhibited. They seemed to be able to think faster.

Tom was examined and told his teeth were in bad shape. He was also surprised to learn he weighed 145 pounds. He'd been over 190 when they left Japan.

He was interviewed by a personnel sergeant in a large hall filled with tables and chairs. By some miracle of organization, the clerk had Tom's military records in a folder there on the table between them. The clerk reviewed each item with him, dates of travel, days of leave, and the clerk quietly commented or asked questions for clarification and made small notations. He even listened to a long story of explanation after he told Tom he was curious why with a heavy weapons MOS Tom had not earned a CIB. The record's clerk said he'd change Tom's MOS back to Bandsman if he liked. He explained it would be a better MOS if Tom happened to be called back to active duty after his discharge. Tom said, "OK," as he agreed he'd have a better life as a Bandsman.

This concluded, Tom and the rest went back to the barracks. They sat and talked when they weren't sleeping and a couple of days later, they entrained for Pusan.

Pusan was an enormous grey port city with cranes and shipping crowding the docks. Lots of dusty looking workers squatting and Matching the coming and going. Lots of coal dust. Korean boats rusty and listing. The smell of fish and feces.

The soldiers carried their duffel bags from the train through narrow muddy alleys and up a long sloping gangplank into an enormous ferry boat.

They stood at the railings and looked over the smoky roofs of the port. The ocean breeze was cool and moist. An Army tug pushed them out away from the pier and then turned back as the ferry picked up speed pushing through ranks of fishing boats and other vessels of all shapes, sizes, and conditions of seaworthiness.

The soldiers made their way back inside to benches

where they arranged sleeping nooks with their duffel bags, and they smoked and slept, and a few talked into the night.

Before dawn they were inching their way past the islands and inlets leading to Sasebo. They awakened and stretched and wished for breakfast. The sea was like glass in the protected water and the bow wave spread out as they reduced speed without breaking the surface of the water. There was a morning mist slightly obscuring the view of the intensely green islands.

The ferry was met by tugs and was eased up against a pier. The men and boys disembarked now several hundred strong with their rumpled khakis and a rainbow of color picked out from the different unit patches on their right shoulders.

It was after 10:00 AM by the time they'd drawn their bedding and had been assigned bunks with springs in the first real military barracks Tom had been in since leaving Japan. They were called out for chow. They answered roll call and at 10:30 filed over to a mess hall gleaming with stainless steel urns and ovens, and bustling cooks and helpers in whites.

They were fed steak and french fries, green salad, and fresh milk. Tom was astonished by the freshness of the food. He'd not tasted fresh milk in eight or nine months. Supposedly, there was to be all of it you could drink but they ran out of the quart containers in the wire milk cases. There were bricks of ice cream for dessert. Tom took one from a box offered by a cook who came to the table where he was sitting. The cook said, "Take two or three to make up for the milk." But Tom was not accustomed to eating so much. He was already full. He'd drunk too much milk. He went back to his bunk and lay down and smoked until he felt better.

There was a PX. Tom looked at all the articles on display but bought nothing. Passes to town were announced for those who wanted them. Tom didn't want to go. His friend said he was going to town to buy a camera. Tom asked him to buy him one too and gave him $30.

Tom went back to the PX and had a beer, but it filled him up so that he went back to his bunk and slept.

Tom's friend awakened him to show him the camera. His friend was very pleased. He'd spent $35 on each of them. They had leather cases, milky, cold-blue lenses. Made in Occupied Japan was stamped on the case.

When Tom opened his camera, the interior showed a litho of peaches and Japanese characters as the camera had been partly fabricated of old tin can stock. Tom wrapped it carefully in a towel and put the towel in the middle of the clothing in the duffel bag.

The military post was beautiful. It was landscaped with green lawns, flowering shrubs, and palm trees. Small bent over elderly Japanese men and women swaddled against the elements, gently hacked and plucked, swept and raked at the flower beds. Tom marveled at the moist cleanliness, the absence of dust, grease and oily dirtiness he'd lived in Korea.

Tom noticed that he'd begun to relax. He lost a tenseness he'd been unaware of until it was gone. He breathed more slowly and deeply. He felt no tedium at all lying hour after hour in the barracks. He'd had enough experiences for a while.

One afternoon he went beer drinking at the PX with his friend. They drank through the dinner hour talking quietly and intensely. They both decided to re-up and stay in Japan. His friend had become reacquainted with Japan on the camera shopping trip. They'd get assigned to a regular Army post like this one, win promotions, set up housekeeping with some agreeable Japanese girls. They'd wear geta and kimono on their off duty hours. They'd become domesticated. They'd live high on the hog with their PX purchases to exchange on the black market. They'd travel, they'd see it all.

They made their way to the office of Officer of the Guard, a Black captain who received them courteously. Tom made a formal request that he be permitted to re-up in Japan rather than continue on to his eventual arrival in Oklahoma and release from active duty. The captain asked them both to sit down and offered them cigarettes and asked them why they wanted to do this. They said they liked Japan better than Oklahoma and it looked like their chances were probably better in the Army than out of it.

The captain responded mildly that he respected their decision, but quite frankly, they'd been away from home for a while, that they owed it to their families and the people who cared about them to go home for now. After they'd had a chance to reflect on some of their experiences maybe they might still want to re-up and maybe they might want to get some more schooling.

The quiet courtesy of the captain made an impression on Tom and he made no further effort to re-up or to reopen the conversation. Tom thanked the captain who wished them good luck. Tom stood, saluted, and then he and his friend went out of the office into the night quite weary. They were drained and made weary by the excursion into attempting to influence this once the direction their lives would take.

The next day they exchanged any remaining military script for U.S. currency. Tom received a $100 bill and a bit more. He felt odd carrying that bill around. That afternoon they embarked on the MSTS ship somewhat smaller and much cleaner than the one that had transported Tom to Japan.

There were a large number of officers and a contingent of Marines. The Marines settled in and spent the next 11 days polishing their boots.

Initially, there was some kidding about gyrines and grunts but these men returning home were strangers to one another and there was no community from which one could venture and feel secure in bellowing insults or challenges.

CHAPTER 22

The ship was clean. The food was not great, but it came three times a day and they sat down to eat. There was a canteen open a few hours a day for cigarettes and toilet articles. The Ritz crackers and candy were gone the first couple of hours it was open. The weather was sunny and warm. The ship rolled and pitched comfortably throbbing through the green Pacific. The ship had left Sasebo in the late afternoon and the gentle cruise through the numerous islands had revealed scenes of incredible charm and beauty. The sky had flamed red and then purple, and the experience was held in Tom's memory as something he had been extremely privileged to see.

The Marines sat on the hatch covers in their peculiar light green fatigues and spit shined their boots. Hour after hour they spit and rubbed until the boots looked as if they were made of glass. A few obstreperous Marines declared themselves warriors and told anecdotes of their martial experiences. But for the most part nothing at all was said about the previous months' experiences by soldier or Marine.

They smoked, they slept, they ate. The weather became chillier, the sea rougher and greener. There were breaking waves with the wind blowing off their crests in a white spume. The soldiers went back to their duffel bags for field jackets and on deck sought shelter from the wind.

Tom and his friend spent a lot of time talking about

food and they finally agreed after proposing and discarding many suggestions for the first food they'd buy when they got off the ship at the first opportunity that presented itself. A suggestion for a food that wasn't the favorite food or even the most delicious, or intriguing, but the food that would best satisfy a craving for flavors and textures they missed the most. A bacon, lettuce, and tomato sandwich with mayonnaise on lightly toasted white bread. The crisp freshness of the lettuce, the tart freshness of ripe tomato, the crisp smoky unctuousness of the bacon, the sweet tartness of the mayonnaise met the desires unsatisfied by mashed potatoes, canned green beans, boiled chicken and canned peaches.

There had been the rumor that perhaps the transport might stop in Hawaii, but it did not. Then early one morning it was announced that the coast of northern California was visible. Sure enough, on the horizon ahead, low irregular shapes were visible.

The men clustered in areas where land was visible as the ship drew nearer over the next couple of hours. To the port side high cliffs could be distinguished from the land mass, then the Golden Gate Bridge, and the white rectangles of buildings against a green landscape; on the starboard a sandy beach, the San Francisco light ship. They could make out automobiles crawling smoothly between the buildings.

The pilot left the bobbing pilot ship in a small boat that wallowed and smashed through the waves to a ladder lowered from the transport. A stocky, elderly man in a dark blue raincoat made a light-footed skipping step from the small boat to the platform at the bottom of the ship's ladder. The small boat curved away with a burst of speed and raced back to the pilot boat.

The ship sailed under the bridge, tall cliffs on the port side, the green cedars of the Presidio on the right. Tom admired the homes, some were mansions, ranging from the shore, up steep hills on the San Francisco side. Tom saw people walking and standing, buses, cars. Tom wished very much to be with them exploring that beautiful city. The troops were ordered below as the ship was met by tugs and was pushed alongside a wharf and one of the long yellow warehouses of Fort Mason.

A young woman stood on a small platform singing some popular songs. There were a scattered few other spectators, some in uniform, some civilians who waved a welcome to the ship. The troops below sat on their duffel bags until ordered up the metal stairs to disembark.

They walked down a long gangplank to the asphalt pavement alongside the ship. They were told to go into the warehouse where milk and doughnuts were being provided by the Red Cross. Tom had a sticky sugary doughnut and a carton of milk handed him by a well-dressed older woman, one of several serving from a folding table. Tom thanked her and she briefly acknowledged his thanks half-turned away talking to another woman.

The young woman on the platform finished a last song, stepped down, and walked away. Someone picked up the sound equipment, rolled up the long electric cords that had run across the asphalt and carried all that away. Some grey Navy trucks came and got the Marines. There were a few waves of farewell exchanged with the soldiers. Tom had made no acquaintances on the trip home. Some other troops were marched away to the barracks and administration buildings of Fort Mason.

Only the men and boys of the 45th were left. The several hundred were marched through the warehouse to another wharf where a huge old-fashioned Bay passenger ferry was tied up. They went aboard and lay their duffel bags on the long benches and then clustered at the rails to look at the city that was to be denied them. The Bay was filled with pleasure craft and freighters. Someone pointed out Alcatraz, the Rock, with its water towers and the immense yellow fortress of a prison.

The ferry boat's engines shuddered the boat away from the dock with an enormous upwash of green water. The crew coiled the lines and then disappeared. Tom thought he'd like a job working on a ferry boat or a tug.

The ferry pushed itself through the Bay north to where the channel narrowed and there were small inlets with interesting homes and dark greenery. Then north of that past brown yellow golden hills, past shipyards and tank farms and past other ferries. As it grew late Tom went inside to sit and doze on a bench while those around him played cards or slept.

Tom slept also and when he awakened it was dark. The ferry had stopped or was drifting and then there was a thundering roar as the ferry backed and a good solid bump as it came to rest.

Tom got up and looked around in the dull yellow light as the men gathered their gear and dragged it down the steps to get ready to leave. They walked off the end of the ferry in its slip and formed ranks and their names were called. Eventually, they were all on trucks for a 10 minute ride through the streets of a small river town, streets lined with bars and furniture stores and gas stations.

They came to the Army post, the gates flanked with stone pillars. A sign proclaimed this was Camp Stoneman. Going through the gate Tom could see he was in a classic Army post of the Camp Polk kind for the first time since Louisiana. There were two-story yellow wooden barracks sitting on concrete blocks and between the barracks bare earth or straw-colored grass. There was a frame post chapel. There was no landscaping of any kind, no trees, only the stark buildings. They drew up at a barracks and filed in each to claim an empty bunk. Some were occupied already by soldiers sitting around in their undershirts, reading magazines, and listening to the radio. This was the first time Tom had been in a barracks that tolerated the cacophony of radios. There were at least three playing at moderate volume, loud enough to compete with one another and all three tuned to different country music stations.

Tom had no idea where he was. He'd never heard of Camp Stoneman. Obviously, they'd traveled several hours from San Francisco in a generally northern direction bearing east. But he had no idea where Stoneman was. A sergeant had told them they'd be there for up to a week for further processing before they'd entrain for Oklahoma.

They were given directions to the mess hall where they could probably still get sandwiches for supper. They were told they were restricted to the post and there would be no passes granted.

On the way to the mess hall some of the soldiers asked passersby which direction it was to town. They promptly headed in that direction. Tom later learned that they'd climbed a fence when they got to it, crossed a ditch filled with dry weeds, located a road and then walked into town which was not much. They'd drunk beer at a couple of really seedy bars with nothing but hillbilly music on the jukeboxes. Then for lack of anything better to do had walked back to the post, climbed the fence and had gone to bed early.

Tom himself went to eat at what turned out to be a gymnasium-sized central mess hall where a few dead-tired KPs and a cook dealt out sandwiches and cake while asking them if they were, in fact, the group they'd held the mess hall open for and then locked the doors and turned off most of the lights. Then they sat wearily waiting for them to eat and leave. For those KPs the day had begun before 5:00 AM and now it was after 10:00 PM.

The next morning Tom ate breakfast, a good one. There was no way to generalize about Army chow. It ranged from wholesome, plentiful, and delicious to merely life sustaining, to inedible—some of the variety meats and the uneviscerated frozen chicken.

The soldiers reported to an auditorium where the gathered EM and officer rotatees, it was announced, would be receiving information helpful to them upon their return to their homes, whether it was to return to civilian life or to other military assignments. A middle-aged colonel with thin blond hair and gold-framed glasses explained that there would be a full program designed to prepare them to discuss their roles in the United Nation's effort to contain the aggressions of the communists in the Far East which represented such a critical threat to the freedoms of peace-loving people all over the world and particularly those living in the democracies allied with the United States.

This discussion began, Tom saw, to turn into an unbearably long TI&E session similar to the ones he'd suffered in Louisiana and Japan each Saturday morning after inspection and before those with passes were permitted to leave. At least they'd been spared that in Korea. Troop Information and Education. The program designed to provide the political ideology to see Tom, his comrades, and their loved ones through the geopolitical rough spots. It was all incredibly cut and dried as the colonel read from his lesson plan, pointed out relationships on a chart, as the theater was darkened and the men and boys saw films of Russian tanks rumbling over presumably violated frontiers, as they saw images of Christ-like, minus the beard, long hair, and cross, GIs in clean fatigues and spotless clean gear superimposed on flapping Old Glory.

Tom dozed.

During one break there was a recruiting sergeant at a card- table set up in the foyer of the auditorium. Tom walked over and confirmed that if he were to re-up he would be sent back after his leave for a six-month tour in Korea before any other assignment. Tom wearily dismissed, finally, plans to stay in the Army. It was not worth it.

The meetings in the auditorium continued. Somehow the control system of the camp rounded them all up and assured their attendance. Once the colonel was joined on the stage by several officers who were to second his performance. The performance that was to provide the answers doubting parents, spouses, or other inquisitors might demand from them, and especially to neutralize any bitterness, or apathy, or dissent the soldiers may have acquired along with adverse and negative feelings toward cold, fear, filth, pain, exhaustion, and death.

One or two of the officers on the stage repeated the colonel's phrases that the men and boys had served nobly and proudly the cause of the greatest nation on earth of which, undoubtedly, they felt a stirring, bursting emotion when Old Glory preceded the ranks and files of the best damn fighting men in the history of the world, and who would make sure their buddies and their buddies' buddies had not sacrificed or died in vain.

One dark-browed captain's turn came, and he hunched down over the microphone and shot a glaring glance at the assembly and said, "Gentlemen, I've got just one word to add," a moment's pause, "bullshit!" And he turned and walked off the stage. The soldiers roared their delight.

The colonel smiled weakly and gestured toward the exit the captain had taken and added, "Well, the Captain had had his chance too. Free speech is what this country is all about."

The meetings went on for another day and a half. A great breakfast, roll call, march to the auditorium, a great lunch, nap in the barracks, roll call, a great dinner, hillbilly music on at least three portable radios in the evening. The stories of the fence climbers as they returned. Lights out.

One morning instead of the auditorium, they were marched with all their gear to a warehouse platform by a railroad siding and waited as a long line of dusty Pullman cars backed its way toward them.

They were ushered into the cars by smiling effusive Black men in white jackets who greeted them and said if they needed anything to just ask for George.

The morning was bright and hot, the hills beyond the post straw-yellow under an intensely blue sky. The men and boys opened the Pullman car windows and leaned out taking a good last look at Camp Stoneman.

The train seats were wide and comfortable. Their duffel bags were stored out of the way. They explored the toilets and vestibules. They liked what they saw. This was great. The engine whistle shrieked, the cars jolted, the clack increased in tempo. The men and boys loosened their collars and slept.

While at Camp Stoneman Tom bought a roll of film and asked someone to take his picture after he had put on freshly laundered khakis and he'd pinned his ribbons and badges on his shirt. He had stood looking into the sun holding a cigarette. Tom had thanked the soldier for the favor and then wrapped the camera in a towel and put it back in his duffel bag.

Toward the middle of the afternoon a smiling porter appeared at one end of the car and invited them to lunch in the dining car. They hastily put on their shoes and combed their hair with their fingers and followed the porter to the dining car where white jacketed waiters assisted them in being seated. The waiters inquired if they would like coffee or milk to drink and they appeared to set the orders expertly before the subdued soldiers.

A dining car manager in a black suit and bow tie was stationed at one end of the car and severely supervised the service of the meal. On occasion he strode forth to rearrange a glass, or center a plate, or to wish a table a good afternoon.

The soldiers waited rather tensely to see what would happen next. They opened small cellophane packages of crackers and began eating them.

A waiter placed a wide shallow bowl of clear soup before Tom. He took an astonishingly heavy silver soup spoon and ate the half cup of liquid from the bowl. It tasted of chicken. The soup plate was removed and a plate of poached chicken, mashed potatoes and gravy, and peas was placed before him. He ate the peas, some potato, and a bite of chicken, and he was full. He was conscious now that he was riding facing backward. The dining car rocked and swayed. The landscape receded and Tom turned in his chair to avoid the stimulus that made him slightly dizzy. The car was warm. There was an intense smell of food. Tom's table mates were eating noisily and had become comfortable with the formality of the table setting that earlier had caused their watchful waiting. They were calling for more coffee or rolls and butter. Some began to smoke cigarettes as they ate and to ask waiters if there was any source of liquor. Tom got up and went back to the Pullman car. He washed his face and splashed water on his arms and neck. He didn't feel well.

By that evening when the porter began pulling down the upper bunks and making up the beds Tom was ill along with ten or 15 others in his car. They vomited, they had diarrhea. They stood in lines to use the restrooms. They were feverish and unhappy.

Tom ate nothing at all the next two days. He went to the dining car once or twice and tried to drink some fruit juice, but he gagged. A few sips of water would stay down but nothing else would. He couldn't smoke. Cigarettes made his vertigo worse. He slept during the day, at night fitfully kicking the sheets and blanket, getting up to stand in line for the now reeking restroom which the porter, in horror, had abandoned to excrement and vomit. At night Tom sometimes half-lay on his elbows and knees trying to relieve the fits of dizziness.

The third morning of the journey Tom awakened hot and still tired, but for the first time really hungry and thirsty.

He dressed and washed, had a cigarette, and walked with the other soldiers to the dining car. He ate everything that was served. Grapefruit juice, scrambled eggs, bacon, toast, milk, and then he smoked a couple more cigarettes in the vestibule enjoying the mild mid-morning breeze and the rocking of the car.

A soldier came through collecting, he said, tips for the porters whom, he said, otherwise missed out when they worked troop trains. Tom gave the soldier two dollars, and then wondered if he were a fool. He felt that in some way the porters were serving their country too and were sharing in the so-called sacrifices he'd been so thoroughly lectured about. Ever since his travel papers had been conned out of him on that train to Atami, he was a bit nervous on trains anyway. He wondered if the porters got the money that was collected.

It was still morning when the train arrived at Fort Sill, Oklahoma where the Guardsmen were to be released from active duty. The soldiers disembarked and stood under the heavy heat of what promised to be a scorchingly hot day. They rode in olive drab school buses to a tent city, wooden frames with tents stretched over them, the tent sides rolled up to release the heat captured by the canvas and to allow any unlikely breeze to circulate.

They were processed rather efficiently by obviously experienced personnel people. Tom was paid in cash up-to-date and for the 40 some odd days of accumulated leave time that there had been no opportunity to take.

Tom now had almost $300 to see him into civilian life.

All of the arrivees were given three-day passes effective that very evening to go wherever they wished before they'd be expected to return for the final physicals and interviews required before release. Tom went back to his tent and took his duffel bag and found the bus stop that would take him from the post into the town of Lawton.

Tom got off the Army bus at the Trailways bus station, snack bar, newsstand, community center and bought a ticket to Oklahoma City. He'd decided to go to his grandmother's and see what kind of welcome he'd get.

Tom sat in the bus station for several hours with its fans moving the hot air around until the bus arrived with a whoosh of air brakes. The bus driver cowboy came in the waiting room and after a visit to the restroom, picked up some packages and went out and pulled luggage out from under the bus from the luggage bins, and then punched the tickets of the new passengers. Tom got on the bus, stowed his duffel bag in the overhead rack and sat back in a dusty seat of the nearly empty bus for the ride to Oklahoma City.

They drove on two-lane roads past oil wells, fields of wheat stubble, past wooded bottom land, through a series of small towns where elderly men in clean overalls got on or off the bus. Packages and greetings were exchanged by the bus driver and the station agents who seemed to be for the most part heavy set women in housedresses.

It grew dark. The bus raced through the night, its

headlights picking out the reflectors that indicated turns in the road or railings by culverts.

The bus made its way into Oklahoma City through the district of auto wrecking yards, then the cheap commercial district with lots of small neon signs, and then the bus station, the bus docks, loiterers, young mothers with sleepy children, cardboard boxes tied with rope, and sailors.

The driver stepped down first and gave Tom a hand as he left the bus. Tom stretched and carried the bag with him to the restroom where he urinated and washed his hands and face. It was a hot night. Insects crawled on the sidewalk and flew buzzing against the lights.

The city buses had stopped running so Tom went to a Veteran's Cab and leaned in and told the man sitting there where he wanted to go. The cabbie pushed the flag down, said to hop in, and they pulled away from the station headed for 17th and McKinley.

The cabbie sat up straight and seemed to enjoy driving. He asked if Tom had been gone long, and Tom answered a little over a year and a half. The cabbie said he'd been gone three and a half years in World War II. Tom sat on the smooth leatherette seat and listened to the meter tick.

When they arrived at his grandmother's Tom paid the driver and took his duffel bag and walked to the familiar front porch with its wooden porch swing. The night was hot and still.

Tom rang the doorbell repeatedly knowing that it would have to awaken her. Finally, he heard some stirring and then an inquiry behind the door as to who was there.

Tom said, "It's me. I just got home today."

The door was unlocked, and his grandmother undid the screen door. A sleepy little grey-haired woman in a bathrobe. Tom kissed her cheek and she smelled of face powder and bedding. She preceded Tom up the stairs and asked if he were hungry, but he said she should go back to sleep, he was sorry to awaken her. She got the electric fan from the front room, and towels and soap, and she said, "Goodnight," and Tom replied, "Goodnight."

He took a bath and then went and lay on the bed with the fan pushing a breeze across his body. He sank into the soft bed. He didn't awaken until almost noon.

Tom's grandmother said she didn't know what he'd planned for the day, but she was glad to see him. She asked him how many eggs he wanted, and she fried two in a little aluminum frying pan that he remembered. She set out toast and butter and jelly and poured him a glass of milk. She said she would be going shopping and asked Tom what he wanted for supper. Tom said anything would be fine. He looked out the kitchen window to the street shaded by tall elms that held in a bit of the earlier morning freshness.

While he ate, his grandmother bathed and came out dressed in her shopping dress smelling of bath powder. She asked if she could drive him anywhere and he said, "No," adding that he'd see her that evening.

As soon as she left Tom lighted a cigarette and went out on the porch to smoke it. Later he walked to the city bus stop and waited for the loose-jointed bus that jolted over the bumpy asphalt streets taking Tom back downtown.

Tom went to an early movie. The marquee proclaimed the theater to be cooled by refrigeration. Tom sat in the movie house. It was quiet and comfortable. The figures flickered on the screen until it was over.

He stood in the shade of an awning and smoked a cigarette and then jaywalked to another theater across the street, bought a ticket and settled deeply into a seat of another theater cooled by refrigeration.

Tom watched a noisy sentimental Technicolor musical and let his mind go blank until that movie was over also. He walked leaning forward back up the aisle and hesitated just a moment before going back out into the heated punishment of the city street.

Tom walked to a corner drugstore and stood by an open door where cool air fanned out onto the sidewalk. He stood there and smoked cigarettes.

He heard his name. It was an acquaintance from high school. Tom said, "Hello." The boy said that he thought it was Tom, but he wasn't sure.

FINIS

In later years Tom thought back to his military experience and marveled that it had contributed in a positive way to the political and military aims of the United States and the United Nations police action. Nonetheless, the war was concluded by armistice on July 27, 1953.

Made in the USA
San Bernardino, CA
19 November 2019